Ralph Borton
0121 763 3280

LANDMARK COLLECTOR'S LIBRARY

WINDMILLS
A pictorial history of their technology

Rev. Dr. Richard L. Hills

LANDMARK COLLECTOR'S LIBRARY

WINDMILLS
A pictorial history of their technology

Rev. Dr. Richard L. Hills

Landmark Publishing

Published by

Ashbourne Hall, Cokayne Ave
Ashbourne, Derbyshire DE6 1EJ England
Tel: (01335) 347349 Fax: (01335) 347303
e-mail: landmark@clara.net
web site: www.landmarkpublishing.co.uk

1st edition

ISBN: 1-84306-189-9

© Rev. Dr. Richard L. Hills 2005

British Library Cataloguing in Publication Data: a catalogue
record for this book is available from the British Library.

Printed by Cromwell Press, Trowbridge, Wiltshire

Design & reproduction by James Allsopp

Front cover: Stanton post mill, Suffolk
Back cover, top: The row of triple-lift mills in Tweenmans polder, the Netherlands
Back cover, left: A grey runner stone in Cross-in-Hand post Mill
Back cover, right: Archimedes screw at Arnhem Open Air Museum

Page 1: Spring sails on Stocks Hill Mill, Wittersham
Page 3: The rear of a wipmolen

Contents

Preface

My interest in windmills started as long ago as the Second World War when I was staying with my grandparents at Lavant, near Chichester. We children were taken up to the derelict Halnaker Mill on the top of the South Downs where I well remember being fascinated by the massive wooden shafts lying outside. Photographing windmills started in the early 1960s through studying the history of the drainage of the Fens and subsequently lecturing on Industrial Archaeology in Manchester. Working in East Anglia in 1990 gave the chance to visit the many mills in that region including those on the Norfolk Broads, some of which I had already photographed many years before when sailing there. This led to the surprising discovery that no book had been published in Britain covering a general history of windpower, resulting in Cambridge University Press producing in 1994 my *Power from Wind, A History of Windmill Technology*. The present book is a supplement to that one, being a pictorial record of a wide variety of mills in this country and overseas to show how the technology of traditional windmills has evolved over the years. Many more mills have been visited than the hundred or so British and over fifty foreign ones which are contained within the confines of this work. This offering is a small tribute to the millwrights who built the mills and to those who so lovingly maintain and demonstrate them today. I have derived great pleasure from looking at these amazing machines which I want to share through these pictures. I hope to encourage other people to give their support to the preservation of these wonders of our industrial heritage by going and visiting them.

Richard L. Hills,
March 2005

Introduction

The windmill was the greatest triumph of medieval technology because it successfully harnessed an uncontrollable force of nature. These machines arouse a special fascination, standing prominently above the surrounding countryside or townscape, defying what nature throws at them and turning the unseen force of the wind into something useful. Most of the time in England, winds are comparatively light so that the sparse density of the air means that a large structure is necessary to obtain reasonable power. But this makes windmills vulnerable in times of storm, necessitating a sturdy construction. Perhaps this is why many windmills had long working lives and accounts for the survival of so many remains of mills which have been left to decay slowly. Where once there were perhaps over ten thousand windmills across Britain in their heyday in the middle of the nineteenth century, their numbers have been more than decimated so that now those with any machinery left must be much less than five hundred although the ruinous stumps of many more remain. Those same forces of the wind which were once their raison d'étre have brought destruction through driving rain causing timbers and eventually brickwork to rot and collapse.

The first people to employ the power of wind other than for propelling ships or to help winnowing grain were the Persians. To the East of that country in the region of Seistan, the wind blows strongly from the north from mid-June to mid-October. It is possible that the horizontal windmills in that region may have been developed as early as A.D. 644. They were certainly in existence here three hundred years later and were used for grinding corn. In such mills as survived in this region into the 1970s, and a very few may still survive, a pair of millstones were housed in a chamber at the bottom of the mill. They were driven directly by a tall vertical shaft to which the sails were attached along the height of the shaft, radiating from it. Mud-brick walls channelled the wind onto one side of this rotor, so turning it, while protecting those sails on the other side which would have been advancing into the wind. This meant that less than half the sails at any one time were performing useful work. This has always been the disadvantage of the horizontal windmill where the rotor turns in the horizontal plane with the wind blowing across the axle. It has been impossible to establish whether such horizontal windmills inspired the later vertical windmill since the suggestion that these were the source from which the Crusaders developed the western type of mill is doubted and is unsupported by any definite documentary evidence.

Another suggestion is that the western windmill had its origins in watermills described by the Roman author Vitruvius around A.D. 100. These had a vertical waterwheel driving a horizontal shaft. The vertical shaft which operated the millstones was connected to the waterwheel through gearing. However in this case, the water flowed tangentally around the wheel whereas in the case of the western vertical windmill, the flow of air is axial, striking all the sails at the same time. Another suggestion has been that the vertical windmill was derived from a toy which Hero of Alexandria described for working bellows on a pipe organ. A multi-bladed rotor was mounted on a horizontal shaft. The wind blew along the shaft and struck all the blades together. The blades were set at an angle. But a thousand years was a long time for this device to have achieved maturity in the form of the vertical windmill. The manuscripts in which it was depicted are unlikely to have been seen by carpenters capable of building a windmill.

In some parts of the Aegean such as Crete, the wind blows mainly from one direction. Here can be found very simple windmills constructed with a masonry tower in the shape of a horseshoe. The curved front faces the prevailing wind while the rear butts onto the side of a hill. A horizontal windshaft with sails radiating in the vertical plane protrudes from the front of the structure. This shaft drives the millstones through gearing and a vertical shaft in a similar way to a watermill. One disadvantage is that the crude gearing absorbs power but the major disadvantage is that the sails can not be turned into the eye of the wind when it changes direction. It is tempting to see these unidirectional mills as the earliest since they are the most primitive mechanically but there is no evidence for this. The conventional tower mill quickly became established around the Aegean. In these, the horizontal windshaft was mounted in a cap which could be turned round in order to point the sails into the wind. The stones were mounted in a chamber below the cap and so had to be driven by gearing and a vertical shaft. Once again the period when such mills were introduced remains obscure and it is very doubtful whether any existed in this region before A.D. 1200.

Where we are on firmer ground is in Western Europe where documentary evidence shows that windmills appeared here in the twelfth century. While that comprehensive survey of England in 1086, Domesday Book, contains references to over 5,600 watermills, not a single windmill is mentioned. It is highly unlikely that such prominent machines would have been omitted, so the conclusion must be drawn that England contained none at that time. Yet, by an hundred years later, windmills are being recorded in western Europe in the triangle formed by east and south England, Normandy and Flanders. Dates carved into the wooden framework of mills in Flanders may point to this area being an early centre of windmill construction. In the Moulin de Hofland, a beam has been carved with a much mutilated date of 1114. The Moulin du Nord was moved and extensively rebuilt in 1764 but there has survived a clear-cut inscription indicating 1127 as the construction date.

For England, it has been claimed that a windmill at Wigston Parva, Leicestershire, is the earliest known. In 1137, William the Almoner became a monk and decided to make a financial contribution to Reading Abbey by donating his lands, including its mill. There is no mention of a mill here in the Domesday Book but sometime before 1200 Ralph of Arraby agreed that the monks should possess 'the whole windmill' (totum molendinum ad ventum). But there is this long gap of sixty years and the earlier reference could be to a horse or even a watermill since there are small streams in the area. Yet near-by Wigston Magna had a post mill in 1169 which had already been in the possession of two owners. A document of 1155 refers to a windmill in Sussex, possibly Swansborough Manor. Another mention of a windmill is found in the list of the possessions of the Knights Templar at Weedley in the East Riding of Yorkshire which yielded a profit of eight shillings in 1185. Therefore it is evident that the windmill had appeared sometime before 1155 and that it spread rapidly. References have been found to four or possibly five windmills on the Continent before 1200, compared with definitely twenty-three and possible fifty-six windmills in England.

1. The Post Mill

The first question is how were these early mills constructed. The available building materials at this early date were a choice of stone or wood for the main structure. Good building stone was scarce in eastern England while wood was plentiful. We know that the windmill constructed by Dean Herbert at Bury St. Edmunds in 1191 was built of wood. While the wind might be free, tenants were required to have their corn ground at their lord's mill but free burgesses in the town might have theirs ground anywhere. Abbot Samson feared that this mill might take custom away from his own mills and 'grew so hot with anger that he would scarcely eat or speak a single word'. He ordered the Sacrist to send his carpenters to pull down the offending mill and put the timber into safe custody. After an angry meeting with the Abbot, Dean Herbert anticipated the destruction of his mill by dismantling it himself.

The framing for the sails, the shafting, gearing and housing for the millstones would all have been made from wood. All this had to be supported on wooden framing. While this framing might in turn have been built into stone walls, there is no doubt but that, except for the sails, it was all contained within a wooden box called the buck which could be turned in order that the sails should face the wind. The gearing would have called for the skill of a millwright familiar with watermills. The complex structure of the buck would have been beyond the capabilities and knowledge of most village carpenters. The buck had to be supported on a strong trestle framing on which it could pivot, resulting in an absurdly top-heavy structure standing on an absurdly small base yet amazingly surviving the strongest storms and still grinding. Such post mills captured the imagination of medieval scribes who delighted in adorning their manuscripts with pictures of a peasant staggering up to the mill under an enormous sack of corn while a dogs sits on the tailpole watching.

It has been suggested that the buck could have been built around the trunk of a tree which acted as the pivot. But it seems doubtful whether a tree would have been found in a convenient position at the top of a hill. Another suggestion has been that a short, solid tower of stones was built with a post sticking out of the centre, with the post acting as the pivot. The flat top of the tower might support the base of the buck. Such mills have been termed 'paltroks', through their long skirts and may be found in Eastern Europe. Turret mills, with a taller stone base, were once to be found on many of the Orkney Islands. It is suspected that, through scarcity of good timber, the abundant local stone replaced the traditional wooden trestle framing that supported post mills further south.

In the traditional form of the post mill, a tall vertical post rested on a pair of horizontal cross trees set at right angles to each other, with one bar resting across the other. Occasionally there were three cross trees. The lower end of the post was slotted into horns which passed over the cross trees to stop the bottom moving sideways. Each cross tree was carved near its outer end to secure the foot of a quarter bar. These quarter bars sloped in at about 45 degrees and their tops were mortised into the post about halfway up. When set properly, these quarter bars would take most of the weight of the buck down to the ends of the cross trees.

Archaeological excavations have discovered remains where evidently cross trees rested on the ground, sometimes on top of flat stones. This feature can still be seen on the small mills on the Swedish island of Oland. However in this position, there must have been the danger of the wood rotting quickly. On surviving English mills, the ends of the cross trees are supported on short brick or stone pillars, high enough to counteract rising damp. These pillars had another advantage, that of raising the whole mill so that sails of longer radius could be fitted.

Probably most early post mills had open trestles, which presented the least obstruction to the wind. But it was realised that enclosing the trestle with a round house not only protected the woodwork from the weather but also gave additional storage space. In 1303, a windmill

Left: There is a reference to Bourn Mill in a deed of 1636 when it was purchased by Thomas Cook from John Cook so it was already in existence, making it the oldest mill in England. This is also suggested from the shape of its buck with its straight roof and small size, 10 ft. 3 ins. by 14 ft. 6 ins. (January 1974)

Above: Bourn Mill rests on an open trestle with horizontal cross trees and the angled quarter bars supporting the central post well above the ground. The trestle rests on brick pillars which may have been raised when new sails were fitted. (January 1974)

Bourn Mill from the rear. The bottom of the ladder would be raised when turning the mill with the tailpole to face the wind. The size of the door emphasises the small size of the buck. The mill ceased work in 1927. (January 1974)

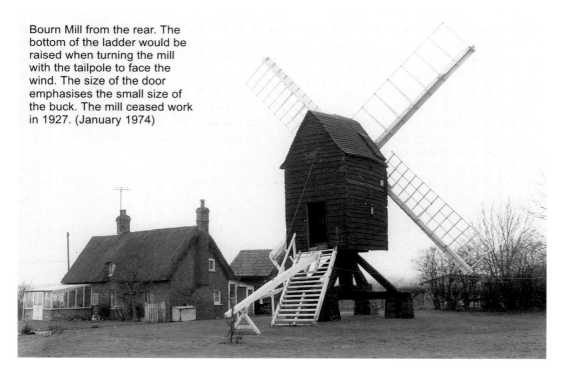

was built on the Westminster Abbey manor of Turweston, Buckinghamshire. The costs of its construction were itemised in the Abbey accounts which reveal that considerable sums were spent on stone, lime and sand for building a wall. There is definitely not enough stone to have built a tall tower so it appears that this wall enclosed part of the mill, presumed to be the trestle. While this may have been an early form of roundhouse, it has been suggested that, through the miller having difficulty in turning the mill, part of the weight of the buck may have rested on this wall. This feature was common later on many mills in the Midlands. At Turweston, to ease the miller's task, the tailpole, protruding from the rear of the mill by which he turned it round, was fitted with a wheel which ran on a circular stone track, the earliest known example of such an arrangement in England.

Normally the whole weight of the buck was taken by the crown tree, a horizontal beam resting and pivoting on the top of the post. It was carved at its centre to fit over a peg or pintle on top of the post. The whole framing of the buck was secured to either end of the crown tree through side girts running from front to back of the mill. Their ends were secured into the middle of the vertical corner posts, which were joined top and bottom by the upper and lower side girts. The top front beam, which supported the main or neck bearing of the windshaft, was called the breast beam and its equivalent at the back, the tail beam. This main framing was supplemented with additional timbers for strength and providing a frame on which weatherboarding could be fitted as well as with others supporting the millstones.

While the sides of the buck normally extended below the tops of the quarter bars to give some protection from the weather, the main floor was situated just above the place where these bars joined the main post. This bottom floor was built on two shear beams, running from front to back of the mill. These formed a collar or bearing around the post which was made round at this point so that it could act as a side thrust bearing. The sails, brake wheel and stones at the front of the buck were balanced by the tailpole and ladder at the rear so the whole turned easily.

The interior of the buck formed the miller's working space. Windows were few and small so there was little light. One either side of the buck told him when the wind changed direction because it would blow in through the appropriate side. In the buck, he had not only to store the sacks of grain which he had to lift up and tip into the hopper from where the grain would trickle down the shoe into the eye of the upper millstone or runner. After grinding, the flour or meal was fed down a meal spout into another sack, which also had to be stored. When grinding the individual sacks of corn brought by each peasant, the cramped space may not have been that much of the disadvantage which it certainly became towards the middle of the nineteenth century when windmillers had to compete with large steam-driven mills at ports where corn from overseas was landed in bulk.

One advantage of the design of the post mill was that it contained only short driving shafts and few gears. Gearing was fitted onto the brake wheel on the windshaft which meshed directly into the corresponding gear or stone nut on top of the shaft or quant driving the runner, minimising frictional losses. On the other hand, as the scale of milling increased, so did the size of the buck. In the nineteenth century, we find mills with two and even three pairs of stones. Customers demanded better quality flour so that flour dressers or graders had to be installed in the already cramped space, or sometimes in extensions to the buck. One answer was to create more storage space by enclosing the trestle framing with a roundhouse. While the roundhouse caused an obstruction to the wind, it could be built high enough to raise the whole mill, enabling longer, more powerful sails to be fitted. Later types of improved sails often replaced the earlier common type so that post mills survived in use even into the nineteen fifties.

The post mill is such an extraordinary structure that it gives the feeling that, had the tower mill come first, it would never have been invented. It could have originated only in an area well supplied with heavy timber to form the post and other main beams. Yet its spread was rapid, particularly in those areas lacking in streams or rivers suitable for powering watermills. It must also have been a boon in those countries such as northern Germany where rivers became frozen up in winter since a post mill could still grind provided there was enough wind. While many post mills in the eastern counties of England were replaced with tower mills during the eighteenth and nineteenth centuries, it was still a viable proposition to move or even to erect new post mills well into the nineteenth century. For example, the large Cross-in-Hand Mill in Sussex was relocated around 1855 while, in East Kent, little Chillenden Mill was newly erected in 1868. Few other machines have been in use, virtually unaltered in their basic principles for over seven hundred years.

Danzey Green Mill being inspected by members of the Manchester Region Industrial Archaeology Society in the summer of 1968 shortly before it was removed from this site for preservation at the Avon Croft Museum of Buildings.
It is a typical Midlands-type post mill in which the buck is supported on the roundhouse.
The framing can be seen clearly since the weather-boarding has fallen off.
(June 1968)

Above left:The horns on the bottom of the central post fit over the cross trees. The post itself is kept upright by the sloping quarter bars at Danzey Green Mill. The pair of horizontal shear beams forming the collar bearing of the buck disappear out of the top of the picture. (June 1968)

Above right: The buck of Danzey Green Mill seen from the rear. At the bottom left of the framing, one of the trolley wheels to support the buck rests on the curb on top of the roundhouse. The post with its iron bands support the main horizontal crown tree. Above it is the brake wheel with gear teeth and brake band around its rim. (June 1968)

Below left: The left side of the buck of Danzey Green Mill. The large side girt rests on the end of the crown tree and forms the basis for all the other framing. (June 1968)

Below right: The lower part of the post in the Cross-in-Hand Mill. The mill was built originally in 1806 and moved to its present situation in about 1855 where it worked until 1969. At either side of the post, the circular roof of the roundhouse reaches well underneath the bottom of the buck to keep out the weather. (May 1990)

Above: The post rises through the bottom floor of the buck at the Cat and Fiddle Mill. Behind it are two sets of stones and their meal spouts, unusually in this case side by side. The flyball on the governor can be seen below the left set.
(June 1990)

Left: The cast iron bracing and bearing fitted to the top of the post on Saxted Green Mill. (May 1990)

Chillenden post mill was built in 1868, the last of its type in England. There was little alteration in design over the centuries except for the spring sails to help regulate the speed. The mill last worked in 1949 but, in spite of subsequent restoration, it collapsed while being repaired in 2004. (March 1991)

Above: Open trestle and tailpole on a Dutch post mill. (August 1994)

Below: There had been a mill on this site at Rolvenden before 1556 but probably not continuously. A date 1772 is carved on part of the mill which ceased working around 1883. It was restored in 1957 as a memorial to John Nicholas, son of Mr. and Mrs. Harold Barham and is a typical example of the tall post mills on this part of the Kent and East Sussex borders. (January 1968)

Above left: Winchelsea or St. Leonard's Mill was another fine tall East Sussex post mill with neat weatherboarding, standing proudly at the top of the hill to the north west of the town. It was built around 1760 but ceased work around 1904. Latterly it was winded by a fantail on top of the buck which drove wheels at the bottom of the tailpole carriage. The mill was destroyed by a storm in the 1970s. (January 1968)

Above right: Hogg Hill Mill, Icklesham, commands a prominent position overlooking the English Channel. Built originally at near-by Pett, the mill was moved to its present site before 1791 and worked until around 1932. The front weatherboarding overlaps the sides in order to prevent rain driving into the joint when the mill faces the wind. (January 1968)

Below left: Mountnessing Mill has an elegant curved roof to its buck. The roundhouse is also unusual in having sixteen sides which was originally thatched until around 1919 when tarred boards were substituted. The mill had a working live of 130 years from 1807 to 1937. (May 1990)

Below right: Finchingfield or Duck End Mill rises above the thatched houses in this attractive village. The overlaps of the weatherboarding can been seen at both front and back. It may date to 1756 and was one of at least five or six in the village. The roundhouse is a later addition of 1840. Through a decline in the population of the village, the mill ceased to work during the latter part of the nineteenth century but survived until 1947 when it was presented to the village, since when preservation work has been carried out at various times. (May 1990)

Above: A feature of many mills in East Anglia is the fantail mounted on the carriage at the end of the tailpole. Gearing took the drive down to the wheels which ran on a special circular track of Stanton Mill. (May 1990)

Left: Aythorpe Roding Mill is the largest remaining post mill in Essex. The roundhouse is 24 ft. diameter and the mill is 45 ft. high. It worked from around 1779 to 1935 and was restored to working order in 1981. The roof was recovered with aluminium sheathing in 1970. (May 1990)

Above left: The buck on Danzey Green Mill was supported by wheels on the curb of the roundhouse in typical Midland fashion. The cast iron canister to retain the stocks of the sails was secured to a wooden windshaft which sloped across the top of the buck from the breast beam on the left to the tail beam on the right. (June 1968)

Above right: The Cat and Fiddle Mill was built around 1788 with an open trestle. The stone roundhouse was added in 1841 to provide additional storage when the mill was converted to the Midland type. The mill was not raised but the floor of the roundhouse was dug out to give access below the cross trees. Additional machinery inside the buck such as a flour dressing machine necessitated the rear extension. The mill ceased to operate in 1952. It was tail winded in 1987 and restoration began soon after. (June 1990)

Right: The Midland style roundhouse was generally wider than the buck so that roofing and a skirt or petticoat had to be fitted to the bottom of the buck to keep the rain out. Wrawby Mill standing in its commanding position on the Lincolnshire Wolds dates to before 1800. The roundhouse was added early in the nineteenth century. The mill was brought to a stand-still in 1940 when a sail broke. It was on the verge of collapse in 1961 but restoration commenced under the auspices of a preservation society and flour was ground again on 18 September 1965. The mill is fitted with spring sails. (September 1990)

Left: The large Cross-in-Hand Mill has undergone many changes in fortune since being built at Mount Ephraim near Uckfield in 1806. It was moved to its present position with two storey roundhouse in 1855. The breast and sides of the buck were sheathed with iron sheets in about 1874 to give protection from the weather. In 1969, one sweep of the patent self-reefing sails fell in a storm while grinding, putting the mill out of action. Restoration was undertaken a few years later.
(May 1990)

Below: Saxted Green Mill has been considered as one of the finest examples of an East Suffolk post mill. Although there is a record of a mill in the village in 1287, the earliest date for the present mill is 1796. The roundhouse has been raised three times so it is a steep descent down the tailpole ladder. The mill was modernised with four patent sails and a fantail on the carriage to keep the sails facing the wind. The entrance to the buck is sheltered with a neat roof. The mill is now owned by English Heritage.
(May 1990)

Main photograph: Framsden Mill looks very different today from when it was built in 1760. The roundhouse was added in 1836 and at the same time the wooden windshaft with common sails was replaced with a cast iron one and patent sails. A fantail was added at the bottom of the ladder. The mill stopped working in 1934 but it was not until 1966 that a group of volunteers began restoration. (May 1990)

Insert: The interior of the roundhouse at Framsden Mill showing part of the trestle supporting the post. (May 1990)

Above: The much photographed row of five small post mills on the Island of Oland, to the east of Sweden. (June 1978)

Below left: The weatherboarding on the buck of one of the Oland mills is vertical, as in most other North European mills. (June 1978)

Below right: The trestle on an Oland mill rests on the ground while the post is still supported by quarter bars. Some of the weight of the buck appears to be taken by the collar of the horizontal shear beams. (June 1978)

An example of a larger Swedish post mill in the Skansen Open Air Museum, Stockholm.
Its design is very simple. (August 1974)

Above: The large post mill from Karlstrup, Zealand, now in the Copenhagen Open Air Museum. (August 1965)

Left: Trestle with double quarter bars and tailpoles of the Karlstrup post mill. (August 1965)

Right: Ladder, tail pole and braces on the Karlstrup post mill. (August 1965)

A large north German post mill now in the grounds of the Berlin Technical Museum. It is constructed with massive timbers. (May 1991)

A Dutch post mill with open trestle. (1994)

Left: Rear of the post mill at the Berlin Technical Museum with tailpole ladder along the side of the buck and winch for winding the mill in the foreground. (May 1991)

The rear of the buck of the Sint Annaland post mill on Tholen Island. The sack hoist is fitted with a neat roof. The mill is painted deep red with white edgings. (August 1990)

Above left: The post mill in the Arnhem Open Air Museum, the Netherlands, has a herring-bone pattern of weatherboarding on the front of the buck which would help the rain to run off. (June 1972)

Above right: The Hamse post mill, De Ster, near Wanroij, the Netherlands, has an impressive buck, reached by a long ladder and stout staging. The buck is painted mustard colour with a red and white star and black roof. (March 1992)

Left: Once there were many mills on the fortifications of towns and cities such as the De Put Mill at Leiden, seen here with sail reduced one reefing point. (March 1992)

An extraordinary type of post mill was developed in the Netherlands soon after 1600 for sawing wood. This was the Paltrok. The name is said to have been derived from the flared coats, 'Palts-rokken', worn by the Mennonites who had settled in the Zaan region. The whole mill with its sawing platform was mounted on a ring of rollers and turned round a central post. This mill is preserved in the Arnhem Open Air Museum. (June 1972)

2. The Hollow Post Mill

In the Netherlands, the challenge had to be overcome of how to drive a scoopwheel for draining land which could be mounted only in a trough constructed in one position by a windmill which had to be turned to face the wind. One answer was the wipmolen. In this type of mill, the buck has shrunk since it had to contain only the windshaft, brake wheel with brake and a gearwheel called the wallower on top of a long upright shaft. This shaft rotated in a hollow tube, supported similarly by the trestle of a post mill on which the smaller buck could pivot at the top. At the bottom of the shaft was fixed a second gearwheel, the crown wheel, meshing with the pit wheel on the axle of the scoopwheel. However the structure of the hollow post was complex because the shaft had to protrude through the top bearing supporting the buck and also itself had to be supported in a bottom bearing. The trestle framing was also more complex since the bottom of the hollow post had to be supported above the lower bearing and gearwheels driving the scoopwheel. On the other hand, not only could the wooden framing be procured more easily than stone in the Netherlands but also such a structure would have been lighter than a stone tower, a great advantage in peaty soils.

Wind-powered drainage mills had appeared in the Netherlands around 1400. These early ones may have been tower mills. It is thought that a reference to a drainage mill in 1430 could be to a wipmolen but the first definite mention of one occurs only in 1526. In England, wind-powered drainage mills were being constructed in the Fens during the sixteenth century. There was a windmill on the sea bank at Fosdyk in 1555 which was almost certainly a drainage mill. George Carlton had erected a windmill on the sea bank between Gedney and Sutton Goates to drain his lands which was maliciously destroyed in 1584. This was most likely a wipmolen because William Stowe had sawed through one of its main supporting beams. Later drainage mills were represented on maps with a symbol of a wipmolen. In 1779, Arthur Young published a drawing of an open trestle hollow post mill driving a scoopwheel near Routh, Lincolnshire. Even in the Fens, this design quickly died out in favour of the smock mill.

The hollow post mill was rarely used elsewhere, in spite of the advantage of the large working space at ground level. The only surviving English example is one on Wimbledon Common built in 1817 for grinding corn. In the Orkneys, a variant appeared for driving threshing mills. The sails were mounted on a tall hollow post above the roof of the barn. The drive shaft ran down through the post to the machinery inside. Small hollow post mills were to be found around the coast at salt pans and excavations for clay or gravel but these have long since disappeared.

Right: A wipmolen with thatched base stands among the groups of tower and smock mills at Kinderdyke. The miller is preparing to set the sails. (May 1977)

Above: A wipmolen at the end of a dyke near Leiden. Sometimes the supporting trestle was thatched and turned into a dwelling for the miller. (May 1983)

Right: This hollow post mill in the Skansen Open Air Museum at Stockholm shows how small the buck may be relative to the rest of the mill underneath, but it is difficult to reach the end of the tailpole. (August 1974)

On the hollow post mill, 't Haantje, Weesp, the Netherlands, the sails are tended from the staging, well above the mill and other buildings underneath. (March 1992)

The Nieuw Leven hollow post mill at Hazerswoude, the Netherlands, has tiles cladding the roof. Access to the small buck is by the ladder from the staging which also acts as the anchor posts to secure the tailpoles. (March 1992)

3. The Tower Mill

The origins of the tower mill are hidden in the mists of antiquity similar to those of the post mill. It is tempting to see the earliest type in the unidirectional mills to be found on mountainous ridges in eastern Crete and on the island of Rhodes where the wind blows from the same quarter for nine months of the year and from the opposite one for the other three. With no rotating cap, these 'monokairos' mills are certainly primitive but their priority must be doubted. Also on Rhodes there may still be seen tower mills with cylindrical or parallel sides. The eastern mole of the harbour had twelve to sixteen and the St. Nicholas mole another three or four. They have windshafts mounted in caps which can be turned to face the wind. Around the top of the stone tower just below the curb is a series of holes into which a peg can be inserted and used as a fulcrum to lever the cap round. This was a type of mill which became common throughout the Mediterranean but is thought to have spread from west to east, with dates in southern Europe for Portugal between 1261 and 1325, Spain 1330, Rhodes before 1389 and Gallipoli 1420. Heavy timber was scarce in many of these regions so that the sails had to be based on a lighter framework, braced with rigging from an extension of the windshaft rather like the bowsprit of a ship.

The first tower mills in northern Europe are thought also to have had parallel sides. They may have originated in France in the twelfth century. The earliest record of a tower mill in Britain has been found in the accounts for 1295 of Stephen de Pencastor, Constable of Dover, which contain a reference to 'Et in uno molendino ventrico de petra de nuvo construendo in dicto castro' (and in one windmill of stone of a new construction in said camp/castle). A stone windmill of a new construction certainly suggests a tower mill, as does the large cost of £36.6s.11d. for the mill wall. Windmills provided a convenient source of power to grind corn for the garrisons and inhabitants of castles or towns when under siege. A windmill tower survives at Bamburgh Castle while many mills were built on city walls in the Netherlands.

While it seems certain that the parallel-sided tower mill was the earliest, this design continued for many years in spite of structural weaknesses. The main bearing for the windshaft might overhang beyond the line of the foundations. Although there was more space in the upper floors, the cap needed a large framework to span across the top. Also such large caps and tops obstructed the flow of air. Further, the cylindrical shape could not withstand the buffeting of the wind as well as a cone which transmitted these forces into the ground better.

The batter of a coned tower gave greater stability. The short squat cones of smaller tower mills seem to sprout out of the ground itself with a strength that can defy the strongest storm. But, as more power was required, the mills had to be built higher to accommodate longer sails. The need to catch the best wind was another reason for increase in height. One answer was to build the mill on top of a mound. Cellars in the mound provided more storage space while the sails could still be tended from the top of the mound. But there was a length beyond which sails could be built through the weakness of long stocks so that, as mills became even taller, the sails no longer reached to the ground. In these cases, a staging would be built around the mill from which the miller could attend to his sails. The staging might also act as the place to which the tailpoles could be anchored to prevent the cap turning out of the wind.

The introduction of brick during the sixteenth century, which was readily available in localities such as the Netherlands and eastern England, enable even taller mills to be built. This was partly in response to the change in milling requirements from serving the small-scale farmers in the locality to meeting competition from the large-scale town mills driven by steam. These later windmills needed greater storage capacity for both grain and flour as well as better preparatory and finishing machinery. But it was still necessary to retain the stones on an upper floor in spite of their weight in order to keep the drive shafts short. The floor beams gave some internal bracing to these tall mills. Particularly elegant mills with a curving batter can still be found in parts of Lincolnshire which were perhaps the highest art of nineteenth century millwrights. Their attractive 'ogee' caps gave a better airflow behind the sails. With the introduction of fantails to keep the mills constantly facing the wind and patent sails to automatically regulate the speed, the size of the staging could be reduced.

Stylistic traditions developed in the regions. These became most evident in the design of the caps. Early ones were probably conical. Across England, caps with straight ridges might be found in Kent, boat-shaped ones in Norfolk, onion or ogee types in Lincolnshire. But no two mills are the same. One of the fascinations of windmills is their individuality. They belong to an age before mass-production. They are the work of individual craftsmen which have been altered and adapted over many years of useful employment.

A typical Mediterranean tower mill on the island of Gozo. Xaghra mill was built in 1724. The miller's house is in the square building underneath. The single set of stones almost fill the milling chamber in the tower. The cap is turned internally. (May 1996)

Above left: One of the oldest mills in the Netherlands stands proudly above the village of Zeddam. It was built in 1450 with only two floors. The parallel sides meant that the cap was large and heavy to turn. (March 1992)

Above right: The extraordinary design of Chesterton mill has been said to owe its origin to Inigo Jones although it is now ascribed to Sir Edward Peyto, the then squire of Chesterton Manor. It was built in 1632 with a low stone wall, a ha-ha, around it to keep out cattle. The open lower structure would present less obstruction to the wind. (June 1991)

Left: Although there has been a mill on this site since 1492, the present one at Chapel Allerton dates from around 1760. The weakness of a mill with parallel sides has caused it to be strengthened with iron bands. The thatch on the cap has been replaced with cedar boarding. The machinery was rebuilt in 1900 with the vertical shaft reaching to the ground floor with the great wheel driving a set of stones underdrift. (April 2005)

Above: Old Buckenham Mill was built in 1818 with five storeys. The tower had little batter so needed a large boat-shaped cap which was said to have had eight sails and a fantail. The tower contained five sets of stones. (May 1990)

Right: Stembridge Mill, High Ham, now has the distinction of being the last mill in Britain with a thatched cap. The mill was built of stone in 1822 in an unusual configuration with a tower parallel at the base but tapering towards the top. The cap jammed in 1897/8 and the mill ceased to work around 1908 through competition from the large roller flour mills at ports like Avonmouth. It is now preserved by the National Trust. (April 2005)

These squat mills on Angelesy and the Fylde such as Llynon Mill on Anglesey look strong enough to defy any storms. Built with a boat-shaped cap in the late eighteenth century, the mill was damaged by a storm in 1918 and fell into disrepair in 1937. Anglesey Borough Council purchased it in 1978 and thoroughly restored it so that it commenced grinding again in May 1985. (August 1991)

Above left: Thelnetham Mill was one of the earliest brick mills in its area and was set to work on Christmas Day 1819. It ceased in July 1924. Restoration was completed in 1987 with patent sails and fantail. The height to the top of the cap is 42 ft. on which vertical boarding also forms the petticoat. The tower contained two sets of French burr stones. Since the sails reached almost to the ground, there had to be two entrances, one on either side of the mill so that the miller could use the one which avoided the sails when working. These doors can be seen open. (May 1990)

Above right: Bardwell Mill was built around 1823. It worked by wind until 1925 and by a 1903 Blackstone oil engine until 1941. It returned to commercial operation again in 1985 and was undergoing further repairs in May 1990. It has a neat domed cap with horizontal boarding and petticoat with vertical boarding. (May 1990)

Right: Stow Mill dates from 1827 and worked until 1930. The windows may have been staggered since it was said that a tower is weakened when they are placed one above the other. The fantail was placed on a tall framing so that it needed a long drive down to the gearing on the curb. (March 1990)

Pakenham Mill was still grinding animal feed stuff with a full set of patent sails until June 1971 when it was struck by lightning. It was erected in 1830 with a domed cap that has a gallery round it. The staging has been removed, perhaps when double-shuttered patent sails were installed. The shutters had not been replaced in 1990 so the mill could not work. (May 1990)

Above: Wicklewood Mill is another East Anglian mill of the middle nineteenth century, having been built around 1845 and which just failed to make its centenary, ceasing to work in 1941. It is a slim five storey tower, holding two pairs of stones. Shutterless patent sails and fantail were replaced in 1980. (April 1985)

Below left: Fantail with striking gear for the patent sails at Wicklewood Mill. (April 1985)

Below right: Thaxted Mill was commissioned in 1804 and has been restored to working order again two hundred years later. It was last used commercially in 1910 when it had three pairs of French burrs. The steep inclination of the batter on the brickwork gives a feeling of great solidity. (May 1990)

Above left: Subscription Mill, North Leverton, was built in 1813 by a consortium of shareholders which lasted until 1956 when they were replaced by a limited company. The parallel section at the top of the tower shows where the mill was modernised in 1884 and fitted with larger patent sails in place of the original common ones. The cap has a particularly fine ogee shape with tall finial. (May 1991)

Above right: Downfield Mill was built originally as a smock mill on a low octagonal brick base in 1726. The base was raised around 1859 when a steam engine may have been installed. The cap was blown off on 4 November 1887 after which the mill was rebuilt in brick and worked regularly until about 1958 when the fantail was blown off. Restoration in 1980 included a new ogee cap with metal sheathing and fantail. (April 1985)

Left: Fulwell Mill was built in 1821 on the site of an earlier one. The limestone base was used as a reefing stage from which the mill was operated until 1949. Restoration in 1955 included a new ball-shaped cap and sails. This mill survives as the most complete one in the North East. (June 1970)

The advantages of building a mill on a mound such as this one in Zealand, Central Holland, are not only the extra storage space underneath but also that the sails are raised above neighbouring obstructions into stronger winds. (August 1990)

The mill at Roosdonck, Nuenen, the Netherlands, has been called Van Goch's Mill since it was painted by him. (March 1992)

43

Above left: Offellt Mill, the Netherlands, was being restored in 1992. With its thatched cap, it stands proudly on its mound outside the village. It has been tarred on the side facing the prevailing wind to prevent water penetration. (March 1992)

Above right: Wilton Mill was built in 1821 to compensate for the loss of the Great Bedwyn town watermill after the Kennet and Avon Canal took the water supply. Falling into disuse around 1914, the mill was purchased by Wiltshire County Council in 1971. Restoration included replacing the staging and the metal-framed cap with sheet aluminium. The mill has two common and two patent sails. (September 1990)

Left: The tall Great Bircham brick mill was built in 1846 on the site of a former mill with a bakery. The cream facing bricks were tarred later to prevent damp penetration. The mill is 52 ft. high to the curb with white ogee cap. (June 1990)

Above left: View from the cap of Great Bircham Mill with vertical boarding and iron railings around the gallery. (June 1990)

Above right: Skidby Mill replaced an earlier one in 1821 and was probably raised around 1879 to its present elegant shape, 40 ft. high to the curb. The curves of the ogee cap are boarded with a double skin while the fantail is supported by diagonal bracing. (July 1990)

Right: Wigtoft, another tall Lincolnshire brick mill, was described as 'newly erected' in 1855. It had three pairs of stones and worked by wind until 1921. A crack is developing from the top window through the curb. Lower, a row of holes locates the position of the staging. (June 1990)

Right: Denver Mill is a well-known landmark standing on the eastern edge of the Fens at Downham Market. It was erected in 1835 to replace an earlier mill. The brickwork is rendered to stop damp penetration. The mill was struck by lightning in 1941 when it ceased to work by wind. It retains most of its milling machinery.
(March 1990)

Below left: Moulton Mill near Whaplode is claimed to be the largest surviving tower mill not only in Lincolnshire but in the whole country, standing originally 97 ft. high to the top of its ogee cap. With eight storeys, it was built around 1825 but the sails were removed seventy years later after storm damage.
(September 1990)

Below right: Sutton Mill, near Stalham, is the largest complete one in the country, being 80 ft. to the top of the cap. It replaced one burnt down in 1857 or 1860 but was struck by lightning in 1940 when it was put out of use. Restoration was being undertaken in 1990. (June 1990)

Above left: A Dutch tower mill at Scherpenisse, Tholen Island, on which the comparatively low staging has vertical supports. (August 1990)

Above right: On taller Dutch mills, the staging is supported on inclined beams. The staging also acts as the anchor points for the tailpole winch. This elegant mill at Sint Maartensdijk, Tholen Island, has similar lines to some of the tall Lincolnshire mills. (August 1990)

Right: The impressive De Valk Mill, the Falcon, at Leiden, stands prominently on the city walls. The miller lived in the bottom of his mill which was built in 1743. (May 1983)

Left: This tall brick mill at Ravenstein, near Nijmegen, is one of many similar mills once used to grind corn or prepare malt for brewing and distilling. Its height placed the sails in strong winds without interference from surrounding houses. (August 1990)

Below: Little Cressingham Mill was one of the very few combined wind and watermills in the country. Built around 1821, there were two sets of stones driven by wind in the upper part of the six storey mill and two more in the lower part worked by water. It was tail winded in 1916 so that it did not work by wind after that. Restoration started in 1981. There were other combined mills at West Ashling in Sussex, Hibaldstow in Lincolnshire and Melin y Bont, Bryndu, Llanfaelog in Anglesey. One mill at Kennington, near Ashford, Kent, was powered by wind, water and steam. (June 1990)

4. The Smock Mill

Although 'smock' was sometimes used to describe a brick or masonry tower mill, a smock mill is usually considered to have a wooden skeletal framework with a covering such as thatch or wooden boarding to protect the interior from the elements. The Netherlands is both the home and the probable origin of the smock mill. In the western part of the country, stone had to be imported so that it was expensive, while timber might be rafted down rivers such as the Rhine and so was cheaper. In marshy areas, piling might be necessary to support any building, on top of which it would be natural to erect a wooden structure. Wooden-framed drainage mills may have appeared as early as 1422 which may not have had any protective covering. By 1526, these had developed into 'polder' mills with thatched sides like those surviving today. This was the type which formed the basis for the later Dutch industrial mills.

Normally there were eight near vertical cant posts which formed the main support for the whole structure and gave the mills their octagonal shape. A few were hexagonal. The cant posts might be fixed directly to the tops of the piles or there might be a base, sometimes up to a couple of storeys high on which staging could be fixed to tend the sails. A brick foundation would raise the mill high enough to prevent the bottom of the wood rotting. Weatherboarding might replace the thatch and this was the covering found in England. It is thought that the smock or polder mill was introduced into North Holland and spread southwards. In these more northerly mills, the winding mechanism for the cap is to be found inside, as on early tower mills. The arrangement of the stones for grinding corn was similar in both types.

The smock mill had spread to England before 1638 when the South Lynn oil mill was erected by the Dutch. Such mills were confined largely to the south east of England where the millwrighting tradition in wood survived longest, especially in Essex and Kent. Although the cant posts were cut from massive single pieces of timber and were linked by intermediate framing to make a rigid structure, the buffeting of strong winds caused the joints to move a little. A prevailing wind hitting the structure regularly from the same side not only would force the curb out of the round but the cant posts on that side would be pushed inwards while those on the opposite side would be pushed out. This caused the top of the windward side to sink while the other rose, causing the curb to tilt and the cap to jam.

Although thatch will need regular renewal, it gives a seamless covering all round the mill structure. While in a strong wind the draught may be felt coming through it, rain does not penetrate. On the other hand, weatherboarding must be jointed at the cant posts. While sometimes in the case of a prevailing wind from one direction, the weatherboards may be overlapped to cover joints on that side, normally there is no overlap so some waterproofing material such as lead or tarred cloth strip is laid over the joints. Rain penetration soon causes the timber to rot so the weatherboarding needed regular tarring or painting, causing maintenance to be more difficult and costly than on tower mills. Smock mills deteriorate quickly if not kept in good repair. Yet the millwrighting tradition continued in Kent throughout the nineteenth century, with Stelling Minnis Mill being built by T.R. Holman in 1866 and Willesborough Mill three yeas later by John Hill of Ashford. Then in 1928/9, Holman Bros. built the experimental mill for generating electricity at St. Margaret's Bay, overlooking the Straits of Dover.

Above left: Great Thurlow Mill was originally at Slough, Buckinghamshire, and has a date of 1807 carved on a doorframe. From 1908, the wind was supplemented by a portable steam engine which drove the stones through a pulley on the side of the mill. The sails were removed in 1924 but animal feeds were ground until 1937 after which the mill became derelict. Restoration commenced in 1959 when the vertical weatherboarding was replaced with horizontal. (May 1990)

Above right: The massive cant posts of Sarre Mill are braced with lighter subsidiary framing. The mill was being restored in 1991 when a strong steel curb was being inserted. (April 1991)

Left: Herne Mill is another fine Kent smock mill, built in 1781 by John Holman of Canterbury. The brick base was inserted in 1856 because trees had grown up around the mill and were taking the wind. The staging is possibly a later addition because it obscures a window and door. New sails (sweeps in Kent) were fitted in 1936 after the mill had been struck by lightning. When in full working order, the sails would weigh about 6 tons. The mill last worked by wind commercially in 1952 but was reopened in July 1986 after restoration. (April 1991)

Above left: The early nineteenth century West Kingsdown Mill was moved from Farningham to its present position in April 1880. It stands on a square brick base. It fell into disrepair after ceasing to work in 1928 and by 1950 was in poor condition. However restoration commenced in 1960. (April 1990)

Above right: In spite of the lead strips on the joints of the weatherboarding, water penetration was observed inside on West Kingsdown Mill. The gearwheel on the side of the cap operated the winding mechanism from the fantail. (April 1990)

Right: Interior framing of West Kingsdown Mill. The slot for the spout can be seen at the base of the right hand set of stones through which the meal fell to sacks waiting below. (April 1990)

Above left: This smock mill surviving at Woodchurch was built in 1820 and worked for about one hundred years. It was restored in 1986 with four patent sails. (April 1991)

Above right: Upminster Mill is said to have been made from timbers of captured Napoleonic warships around 1803. It is a fine example of an Essex smock mill with originally three pairs of stones. A steam engine was added in 1818 and five pairs were being worked in 1849. After the mill was struck by lightning in 1889, it was still occasionally worked by wind up to 1930. Unusually for a smock mill, the cap has a gallery. The patent sails have two almost equal rows of shutters either side of the stocks. The mill was restored and opened to the public in 1967. (May 1990)

Left: Union Mill, Cranbrook, on its tall brick base towers above the houses. As built in 1814 for Henry Dobell, it had common sails and the cap turned manually. It was modernised in 1840 with the present patent sweeps and fantail. The tallest mill in southern England, it ran by wind until 1954. (May 1990)

Opposite page: The drive on Union Mill from the fantail passes down the left side of the supporting frame to the gearwheels on the left of the cap. The patent sails are controlled by the chain hanging down the back of the mill to the iron staging. (May 1990)

Above: Dalham Mill standing 50 ft. high is one of the largest on the Cambridgeshire and Suffolk borders. It dates from the last years of the eighteenth century and lost all its sails in December 1802. While still working in 1926, it was in a poor state by 1935. It was an early instance of restoration which was carried out in 1938 and at various times subsequently. (May 1990)

Below left: The age of Earnley Mill is uncertain. In 1827, the wooden structure was raised some seven feet and the brick base inserted with a staging. It was the last working windmill in West Sussex, ceasing in 1946. Twenty years later, it was in a poor state of repair. (April 1967)

Below right: Drinkstone Mill well illustrates the problems of preserving these mills. At least here some attempts have been made to keep out the weather. (May 1990)

Above left: The mill on Beacon Hill was the sole survivor of three in the Benenden, Kent, vicinity in January 1968. Built around 1800, it was worked in conjunction with the Wandle watermill but had ceased by 1914. (January 1968) Above right: The fantail on Beacon Hill Mill protruded a long way to the rear of the cap. The worm gear turning the cap can be seen. The mill was in a poor state of repair at the beginning of 1968 and had disappeared a few years later. (January 1968)
Below: In the south west delta region of the Netherlands can be found weatherboarded smock mills for grinding corn. Among them is this one at Sint Philipsland, Philipsland, with its flared skirt, dating to 1724. (August 1990)

Above left: Bennink Molen, Doetinchem, on its brick base, is covered with wooden shingles. (March 1992)

Above right: Oude Leije Mill, Friesland, has thatched sides. (August 1990)

Left: De Bleke Dood Mill in the Zaan area was built in 1658 entirely from wood. The base is weatherboarded and the body thatched. (March 1992)

The smock mill from Fuglevad, Zealand, in the Copenhagen Open Air Museum, is completely covered with small wooden shingles. (August 1965)

A mill in the Zaan area, the Netherlands, dressed for a festival. (June 1972)

5. Development of the Sails

While the sketches of windmills drawn in medieval manuscripts cannot be relied upon to show accurate representations, they do show that western mills had four sails which fronted into the wind and would be called in modern parlance, 'full admission, axial flow type'. The sails, or blades, were paired, being fitted onto opposite ends of a common stock which passed through the end of the windshaft. The sail might be built upon a main spar, the whip, which was secured to the stock. The actual sail consisted of a wooden framework which was covered with a stout cloth such as canvas to catch the wind. The framework on each side of the whip was called a blade.

To start the mill, the miller had to bring a sail to its lowest position and secure the canvas over it, possibly by climbing up the blade. He than had to spread the canvas on the remaining three in the same way. To set down the mill when he had finished milling, he had to reverse the procedure. Should the force of the wind strengthen and there might be a danger of the mill overspeeding, he would have to stop the mill and shorten sail by reefing the amount of canvas exposed. Early pictures show blades with framing equal on both sides of the whip in a single bay. The canvas was woven in and out of the cross bars and made fast top and bottom. To reduce the amount of canvas exposed, these sails were reefed by drawing the cloth towards the stock like a curtain. As each sail had two strips, this must have been very difficult in a gale or in freezing conditions. A rather inaccurate picture of an English mill for land drainage published in 1652 shows sails with two lengths of cloth, one either side of the whip but not interlaced. This system was replaced completely in the Netherlands during the late sixteenth century. On these later mills with sails where the cloth was spread across the front of the framing, there might be four reefing points, first reef, the least canvas; sword point, about half covered; dagger point, three quarters covered and full sail.

Handling the sails was a tough task. While in summer a windmill in full sail is a glorious sight as the sails reflect the sun, winter conditions could be grim. A traditional windmill needs near gale-force winds to work effectively and the miller had to take advantage of all the wind he had. To reduce sail in a storm, the miller had to go outside and handle the canvas which of course caught not only the wind but also rain and sleet so that water poured down the sail onto him. The canvas had to be rolled up and secured. He might have to adjust the reefing on all four sails in the night, not a pleasant task because he might have to climb up the cross bars to free the reefing points and canvas. The task was made a little easier in parts of northern Europe where wooden boards were used in place of cloth.

Early pictures and these sails with wooden boards reveal that early sails were straight throughout their length so had 'constant weather' with no twist. It is probable that Dutch millwrights perfected the design of the traditional windmill sail during the sixteenth century. Their 'common' sails have remained virtually unaltered up to the present time. They have a small leading edge covered with boards set at an angle to the whip which helped to guide the wind onto the sail. The cloth-covered framing with cross bars usually in three bays was on the driving side of the whip. This framing was twisted, sloping away more steeply from the wind at the windshaft end where the speed of rotation was slowest. The tips will be moving much faster so here there was little inclination from the plane of rotation. This form seems to have been developed empirically based on experience. This new type of sail may have led to the great flowering of the Dutch industrial mill around 1600. Such sails spread to England and elsewhere. In a well-designed sail, there should be a partial vacuum behind the cloth as well as the wind pushing on the front. The body of the mill forms an obstruction to the wind, causing its speed to drop. The canvas will flap passing through this higher pressure zone so that, if raining, the mill will be showered with water from the sail.

Above: The framework on the sails of the windmill at Gozo are equal on both sides of the whip which points to early practice. (April 1996)

It has been pointed out that the miller has to bring each sail to its bottom position to set or reef it. It is possible that in the earliest mills, the sails were turned out of the wind or quartered to stop them. No figures have been found to show how quickly the sails loose power when not facing directly into the eye of the wind. However some form of brake was soon devised. While a few small mills in northern France have a form of clasp brake, all others have a band brake working on the rim of the main gearwheel on the windshaft called the brake wheel which transmitted the power to the rest of the machinery. One end of the band was attached by a link to the framing of the buck or cap. The other end was joined to the brake lever. The brake lever was operated by a simple but ingenious device, a hook suspended from the framing and a rope from the end of the pivoted lever running over a pulley and then to the bottom of the mill. The miller pulled on the rope, raising the lever, freeing the brake while a peg on the lever pushed the hook to one side. Letting the lever down slowly allowed the hook to return and catch on the peg, keeping the brake off. If the miller let the lever down quickly, the hook failed to catch on the peg through inertia, allowing the lever to fall down and pull the brake blocks on.

Wooden brake blocks acting against the wooden rim of the brake wheel might cause sufficient friction if there was too much sail in a rising wind so that sparks were generated which set many a mill on fire. These band brakes were most efficient in the normal direction of rotation as they tended to pull themselves on. But if the wind came from the rear of the mill so that it was tail-winded and the sails started rotating backwards, the brake would tend to free itself and so not hold the sails, another cause of destruction to mills. Het Prinsenhof Mill in the Netherlands had an extra sprag brake in the form of a toothed lever which could be engaged with the cogs on the brake wheel when the mill was stopped to secure the windshaft firmly.

There was little or nothing a miller could do in calm or light wind but wait for it to strengthen. But towards the end of the eighteenth century and into the nineteenth, mechanisms were devised for spilling the stronger gusts so that not only did the mill rotate more steadily but there was less danger of it running away. Also the self-reefing sails allowed the miller to spend more time milling because he did not have to adjust the cloth on his sails. The earliest English patent for some form of automatic regulation was taken out by William Perkins in 1744 but it contains no drawings. The most successful early design originated with the Scottish millwright, Andrew Meikle, who sent John Smeaton a drawing of his proposals on 17 March 1772. The length of the blade was divided into sections and across each section was fitted a canvas covered frame called a shutter or shade. The shutter was pivoted rather like a Venetian blind, so it could present the flat surface directly against the wind or be turned out of it. The shutter was held against the force of the wind by a spring. If the wind became too strong, the shutter was blown open against the spring pressure. As developed for general use, the pivot was moved to one end of the shutter and a lever added. All the shutters were connected by the lever to a common rod or sail bar which was linked to a single spring. The tension in this spring was set by the miller at the beginning of a day's work to suit the power he needed and the strength of the wind. Each sail had to be set separately by bringing that sail to its lowest position and stopping the mill. Once set and running, there was no way of making adjustments. To set down at the end of the day, each spring had to be released. When spring sails passed through the high pressure zone at the front of the mill, they snapped shut, showering the mill with water in wet weather. Quite often, mills were fitted with a pair of common sails which had greater driving power particularly in light breezes and a pair of spring sails which gave a fair degree of regulation.

The system for automatic regulation which became used most generally on English mills was patented by William Cubitt in 1807. The same system of pivoting shutters was fitted to each sail but the sail bars were linked through bell cranks to a common spider on the end of the windshaft. The spider was fitted on the end of a long rod passing down the centre of the shaft. If this rod were pushed or pulled, it would open or shut the shutters. Automatic control was given through the tail end of the striking rod being connected most usually through a rack and pinion to a weight hanging on a chain. To start the mill, the miller hung on the chain a weight appropriate for the power he wanted for that day's work. The weight turned the pinion through the chain, moving the rack and so closing the shutters. A strong gust of wind overcame the effect of the weight, raising it and opening the shutters. If the miller wanted more or less power, all he had to do was to change the weight. The system worked automatically and, in various forms, became widely used in Britain and helped to solve the problem of overspeeding in gusty winds. The maximum length of each sail with wooden stocks and whips is just over thirty feet. Each would weigh about a ton. In a good wind, the speed would be ten to twelve r.p.m. with a tip speed of 30 m.p.h. producing about 12 h.p. The cap and all its associated machinery weighed around thirteen tons.

Millers in the Netherlands rarely fitted spring or patent sails, perhaps because wind speeds were higher and more regular there. But in the years following the First World War, sails were developed with streamlined leading edges to generate power at lower wind speeds. In 1926, a millwright, Adriaan Dekker of Leiden fitted metal sheeting around the leading edge of the whip or stock to streamline that side and carried this round until the sheets joined the framing on the driving side. The driving side was still covered with canvas in the normal way. Other designs followed, such as that by Chris van Bussel in 1934. Longitudinal storm boards had been fitted at the tips of sails on their leading edges much earlier. These became mounted on pivots so that they could be twisted to act as air brakes in strong winds or, when suitably curved, helped to guide the wind around the cloth in weaker winds. So not only would Dutch mills work in lighter winds but could be controlled better. However these developments were rarely taken up in Britain where the age of the traditional windmill had passed.

Left: The Dutch may have introduced sails which had both the framework on the driving side only as well as the twist or weather along their length for a better aerodynamic shape such as those fitted to this post mill at Sint Annaland, Tholen Island. (August 1990)

Right: The sails on one of the Schermer polder mills with the cloth stretched fully, showing the twist along the blade. (April 1994)

Above: A typical Dutch scene with the lifting bridge giving access to Leiden through the ramparts on which was placed the De Put post mill. The sails are reefed back one stage to dagger point. (March 1992)

Left: A field mill with scoopwheel in the Zaan museum area. The wind must be quite strong because only two sails are set at dagger point. (June 1992)

Above left: The framing of a common sail on the Herringfleet smock drainage mill, Suffolk.
(March 1990)

Above right: The framing may be strengthened with back stays as at Stocks Hill Mill, Wittersham.
(January 1968)

Below: The sails on the Fuglevad smock mill have a pronounced twist along their length.
(August 1965)

Above left: The leading wind or storm board is being fixed on a sail of the mill at Offellt, the Netherlands. (March 1992)

Above right: The canvas is being spread on a sail of the Offellt Mill. (March 1992)

Left: The reefing points are being securely tied at Offellt Mill. (March 1992)

Opposite page: Four stages in setting the last sail on the little Marendijk wipmolen at Zweilaan near Leiden. (March 1992)

Above left: One of the brick mills at Kinderdyke with sails fully set. (May 1977)
Above right: A sail set at sword point on one of the Schermer polder mills. (August 1990)
Below: A spare set of shutters for the Berney Arms Mill. (August 1990)

Above: The shutters with wooden framing in the open position on a sail of Thelnetham tower mill. (May 1990). Below left: The end of a sail on Stanton post mill with the operating sail bar and levers above. (May 1990). Below right: With shutters either side of the whip, a pair of sail bars was needed to operate the shutters on the post mill at Aythorpe Roding. Some of the shutters have not been replaced during restoration. (May 1990)

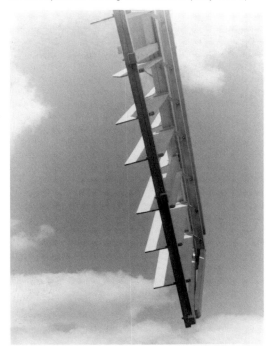

Above: The spring sails on the White Mill, Sandwich, were tensioned against quarter elliptic springs at the inner ends of the stocks and secured at the outer ends. (April 1991)

Below: Chillenden post mill was fitted with full elliptical tensioning springs. (March 1991)

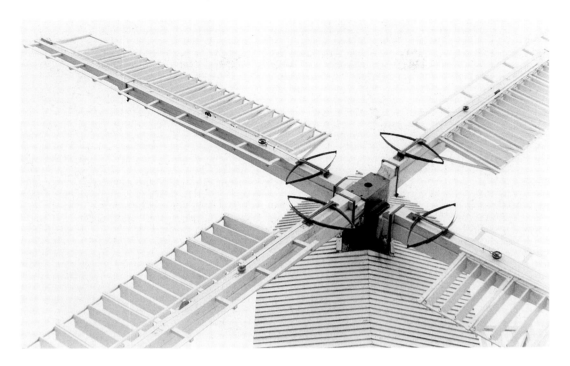

Above: The elliptical tensioning springs on Stocks Hill Mill, Wittersham. (January 1968)

Below left: The tensioning spring was fitted to the rear of the stock on the sails of Mountnessing Mill. (May 1990)

Below right: Looking along a pair of patent sails with double shuttering on Stanton post mill. The sail bars are connected to the spider in the centre of the windshaft. (May 1990)

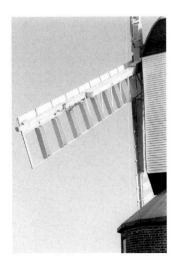

Above: Parts of the linkage for operating the mechanism of Sarre smock mill. (April 1991)
Below left: The sails on Wicklewood Mill with no shutters but with the backstays for supporting the framing for the blades. (April 1985)
Below right: Steel stocks pass through the cast iron poll end of the windshaft on Wicklewood Mill. The front boarding of the cap overlaps that on the side. (April 1985)

Above: Wilton Mill had a pair of common and a pair of patent sails to give better driving power with some automatic control. (September 1990)

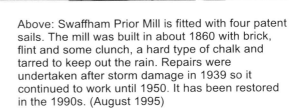

Above: Swaffham Prior Mill is fitted with four patent sails. The mill was built in about 1860 with brick, flint and some clunch, a hard type of chalk and tarred to keep out the rain. Repairs were undertaken after storm damage in 1939 so it continued to work until 1950. It has been restored in the 1990s. (August 1995)

Left: The patent sails on North Leverton Mill look like large paddles, especially when compared with the comparatively small size of the mill. (August 1991)

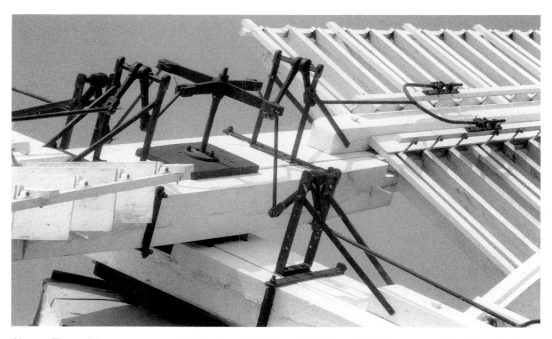

Above: The sail bars are connected to the spider through links and bell cranks on Swaffham Prior Mill. (August 1995)
Below left: The striking rod operating the spider at Sarre Mill is fashioned into a rack which can be moved in and out by gearing. (April 1991). Below right: The cast iron shaft for West Kingsdown Mill has been bored to allow the operating rod to pass down its centre and be linked to a bent lever on the end of which weights could be hung. The small bevel gear in the background was once connected to the fantail for winding the mill. (May 1990)

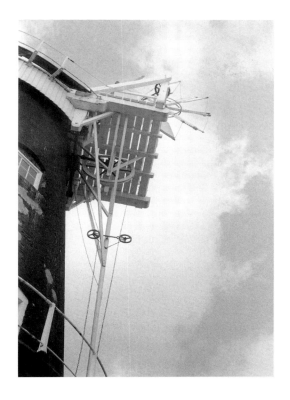

Above left: Below the staging for the fantail of Berney Arms Mill is situated the large wheel for operating the gear and rack on the striking rod for the patent sails. A weight would be attached to the chain hanging from the large wheel to close the shutters. The chain could be tied to the vertical pole to prevent it flailing around in the wind when out of use, still allowing the cap to rotate.
(March 1990)

Above right: The patent sail operating chain has a small weight hanging on it at Alford Mill. For stronger winds, appropriate weights would be placed in the weight boxes on the staging and hung on the chain.
(July 1990)

Left: The corn mill at Reek in Central Holland has streamlined Dekkerised sails.
(August 1990)

Above left: The curved leading board of the sail on one of the Aarlanderveen polder mills helps to guide the wind round the sail better. The storm board has been removed so that there is less possibility of the mill turning when not being used. (March 1992). Above right & below left: Stavenisse Mill, Tholen Island, not only has streamlined sails but automatic storm boards which would turn and act as air brakes to control the mill in strong winds. (August 1990). Below right: Not only are the leading edges streamlined and curved on the mill at Witmarsum, Friesland, but the last section rotates to act as an air brake. (August 1990)

The Agneta saw mill, Ruurle, the Netherlands, is fitted with longitudinal Fokwiek foresails and Ten Have driving sails on one pair of sails with a pair of streamlined common sails for the other in order to give good power and control. (March 1992)

Above: The sails may be stopped from turning by the band brake around the large gearwheel or brake wheel on the windshaft of Het Prinsenhof Mill in the Netherlands. There is an additional sprag with cogs which can be engaged with the gearing on the brake wheel to prevent the sails turning when the mill is set down. (March 1992)

Below: The brake lever on West Kingsdown Mill is operated by pulling on the rope. It is held in the off position by the catch when raised and is dropped down to put the brake on. (May 1990)

6. Multi-Sailed Mills

While early drawings of windmills in northern Europe show them with only four sails, those of mills around the Mediterranean basin are often depicted with five or more. A drawing of 1483 has a couple of mills beside the harbour at Rhodes with eight sails. However one with six sails was recorded at Framlingham in England in 1279. The greater the number of sails, the greater the starting torque, a distinct advantage in light winds. The disadvantage is that the speed of rotation will not be as fast in strong winds because the wind cannot escape between the sails. One blade must not interfere with the air-flow of the others which can happen as the speed increases. Also the greater number of stocks which must pass through the end of a wooden windshaft will not only weaken it but the line of the outer stock will protrude a long way from the main bearing in the cap.

The multi-sailed mill in northern Europe had to wait for the introduction of the cast iron windshaft. John Smeaton claimed that he began the application of cast iron to machinery in 1755. In 1774, he fitted the flint mill at Leeds with five sails. Drawings of Chimney Mill at Newcastle-upon-Tyne in 1782 reveal how he used a cast iron windshaft with a flat cross on its end. The end of the stock of each sail butted against the others at the centre and the back was bolted to the face of one arm of the cross. This method reduced the need for massive pieces of timber to form windshafts while the length of the stocks was effectively halved. The flat cross could be and was applied to mills with four sails as well as six and eight.

Mills on the eastern side of England can still be found with five, six and eight sails. All have patent shutters. It has been claimed that mills with five sails run more smoothly than those with four because four are still driving when the fifth passes in front of the body and loses the wind. But, should one sail be damaged, the mill will be out of action until it can be repaired because, if one sail is removed, the rotor is unbalanced. A six or eight sailed mill has the advantage that, if one sail is damaged, the one opposite can be removed as well and the mill can carry on but with less power. A six sailed mill can be balanced with four, three or even two sails. Six sailed mills became quite popular after the middle of the nineteenth century. There were even a few with eight but, while a four bladed machine should run at about 71% of a two bladed, an eight sailed one would run at only 50% which meant that the internal gearing had to compensate proportionately for the mill stones to rotate at their correct speeds. Increasing the number of blades involved extra expense and complication.

The poll end for the stocks on this six sailed mill on Gozo protrudes a long way over the side of the mill. The thin stocks needed bracing by rigging from a sort of forestay but the number of ropes must have caused severe drag, especially in light winds. Mills with forestays were found on the Scilly Isles and a couple in London but they were never numerous in Britain. (April 1996)

CHIMNEY WINDMILL.

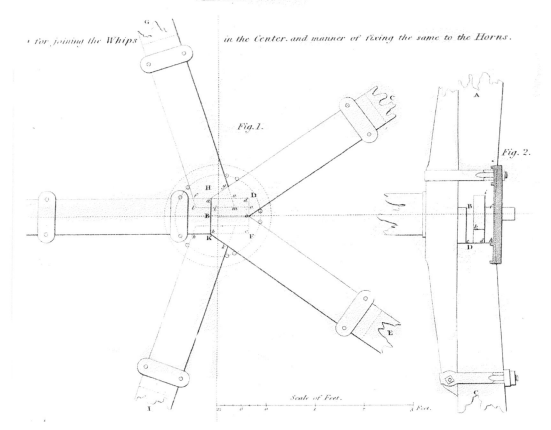

John Smeaton's drawings of the cross on the end of the windshaft for Chimney Mill, Newcastle-upon-Tyne, in 1782 show how he abutted the ends of five stocks and bolted their backs to the 'horns' on the face of the cross. (Smeaton's *Reports*, Vol. II, Plate XV)

Left: The back of the cross on Alford Mill. (July 1990)

Below: The 95 ft. high Hoyle's Mill, Alford, was built in 1815 and worked commercially until 1955. It had two pairs of French burrs and one grey on the third floor with another set of greys being added later. Ironwork and gearing was supplied by Tuxford's of Boston. The mill was set to work again in 1957 by Messrs. Banks, Bros., corn merchants of Kirton Lindsey. (July 1990)

Above left: Dobson's Mill, Burg-le-Marsh is another elegant Lincolnshire mill with ogee cap. Built in either 1813 or 1833, it worked until 1964 and, after being acquired by Lindsey County Council, was set to work again in 1984. (August 1990)

Above right: The sails on Dobson's Mill rotate clockwise, unusually for an English mill. The single bay shutters are very wide. (August 1990)

Left: The Maud Foster Mill in Boston takes it name from the drainage channel passing in front of it. It was built in 1819 for Thomas and Isaac Reckitt at a cost of £1,826.10s.6d with all iron gearing and, with its seven storeys, has been called one of the best proportioned mills in Lincolnshire. With three sets of stones, it could grind three tons of flour a day in a good wind. It worked until 1942 and was preserved in 1953. It was returned to working order in August 1990. (September 1990)

Above: Trader Mill, Sibsey, was built in 1877 by Saundersons, Louth, on the site of an earlier post mill. The height to the top of the cap is 74 ft. 3 ins. After working until 1954, latterly with four sails, the Department of the Environment restored it to full working order in 1981. (September 1990)

Right: Trader Mill after restoration to full working order. The taper of the tower and shape of ogee cap stand out well. The staging has decorative iron railings.

Right: The stone Heage Mill stands on the brow of a hill overlooking the village. It was built in 1791 to supplement a watermill in the valley but was never so reliable. Its two common and two spring sails were blown off in February 1894 when the mill was rebuilt with six patent sails needing 120 shutters. After more damage in 1919, it fell out of use. A preservation order was placed on it in 1966 and the cap sheathed with aluminium a little later. Lightning struck in 1995 which damaged the interior machinery but it was restored again and reopened to the public in 2002. (August 1990)

Below left: The main bearing for the windshaft is supported on a beam across the front of the cap on Heage Mill. (August 1990)

Below right: Brunswick Mill, Long Sutton, was built in 1817 with five storeys and four sails. During the nineteenth century, another floor was added and the mill was fitted with six sails. It ceased work in the 1930s. The remains of the sails were removed by a crane in August 1973. (September 1966)

Pocklington's Mill, Heckington, was built in 1830 with only five sails. The present eight sails, cap and fantail were removed from Tuxford Mill, Boston, in 1892. The mill is 65 ft. high and is the last with eight sails. Each sail is 34 ft. long, 6 ft. wide with 24 shutters in each. It had three pairs of stones and was last used commercially at the end of the Second World War. The name comes from the last family of millers that owned it. Great care had to be taken that the mill should not be tail-winded for fear that the shutters might close with the reverse wind and the sails be blown out of the cap.
(June 1968)

7. Winding the Mill

For maximum efficiency, it was necessary to keep the sails facing into the eye of the wind. As soon as a rotor yaws out of the main wind stream, the blades rotate in a cross-flow situation so that performance deteriorates. This will also affect the blades detrimentally because the angle at which the wind hits the blades will vary all the time, resulting in an unsteady flow over the blades with a loss in power. It may also impose greater stresses on the blades in addition to the normal reversal of forces caused by gravity in each rotation. While one way of stopping a mill may have been to turn the sails out of the wind, should the mill become tail-winded with the wind blowing against the rear of the sails, the sails and cap could be blown off.

Early post mills were winded by the miller pushing against the tailpole sticking out of the rear of the buck. To prevent the mill turning, the tailpole was spragged with a couple of poles. As the bucks increased in size, a winch was fitted onto the tailpole. A lever, called the talthur, raised the bottom of the ladder off the ground to make turning easier. The ladder gave support to the buck. The rope or chain from the winch was tied to one of a series of anchor posts around the mill which prevented the mill turning one way while a second rope would be tied to another anchor in the opposite direction, thus securing the mill.

The sails on tower mills were more liable to turn away from the wind owing to the resistance of the machinery inside the mill. This would tend to make the vertical main shaft remain stationary while the brake wheel and so cap would rotate round the wallower on top of the shaft. Therefore on tower and smock mills it was necessary not only to be able to turn the cap so the sails faced the wind but also to secure it in that position.

The first method of winding the cap was by levering it round from inside. Later the caps were fitted with tailpoles which reached down to the ground. Early pictures show ones with no braces. Braces were secured at their tops to cross beams which passed through the cap while at their lower ends they were joined to the tailpole either towards the middle or at the winch. These may have originated in the Netherlands. In another system, the curb would be fitted with a gear ring into which meshed a pinion mounted on the cap. The pinion was turned by the miller through gearing and a loop of rope round a pulley hanging down from the back of the cap to the ground. If the teeth of the gearing on the curb were external, the drive might be through a worm gear on the cap which had the advantage of being self-locking until rotated. All these methods needed considerable effort on the part of the miller which also took him away from his main business of milling.

In England during the middle part of the eighteenth century, inventors turned their attention to discovering a method for winding the sails automatically. The one which proved to be the most successful and long lasting was the fantail patented by Edmund Lee, of Brock Mill near Wigan, patented in December 1745. His fly or fantail was mounted on framing at the back of a tower mill near ground level. The fly had eight blades fixed to a horizontal shaft. The blades were set at an angle of 40° to 45° to the shaft but later this was about 55°. When the wind blew across the mill at right angles to the shaft, nothing happened, but as soon as it changed to one side or the other, it played on one face of the blades and turned the fly. The horizontal shaft was connected by gearing and shafting to the pinion or worm gear engaging with the gearing on the curb, thus winding the cap. Two thousand revolutions of the fly might be necessary to rotate the cap of a tower mill in one complete revolution. Nine hundred and fifty revolutions of the fly moved the cap on Herne Mill through 90°. The fantail could be left in action day and night, relieving the miller not only of considerable work but also anxiety about becoming tail-winded should the wind direction suddenly change in the night.

Left: The little post mill from the island of Laeso in the Kattegat now in the Copenhagen Open Air Museum is winded quite simply by pushing the tailpole. (August 1965)

Below: The little drainage mill from Adventurers' Fen and now in Wicken Fen has the tailpole strengthened with two braces joining at the bottom where a couple of sprags prevent it turning. (March 1966)

Right: The tailpole of Chillenden post mill is turned by the aid of a wheel. (March 1991)

The winch on the end of the tailpole on the Cat and Fiddle Mill. The lever of the talthur for raising the bottom of the ladder is suspended from the tailpole. (June 1990)

The tailpole, winch, talthur and ladder on Wrawby Mill. (September 1990)

Tailpole, ladder and winch on Sint Annaland post mill, Tholen Island, the Netherlands. (August 1990)

The rear of a wipmolen with the usual layout of tailpole, ladder, braces and captsan winch wheel. The bottom of the wipmolen formed a cosy house with thatched roof. (May 1983)

Top: A typical Kentish cap off Sarre Mill being restored. The poll end of the cast iron windshaft has the striking rod for the patent sails passing through it with fantail to the rear. (March 1991)

Middle left: The finial and boarding on the ogee cap of Great Bircham Mill. (June 1990)

Middle right: The eight storey Hickling Mill built in 1818 before restoration in May 1990.

Right: The temporary cover of Hickling Mill had been removed to allow restoration to commence. The curb with external gearing was being repaired. (August 1990)

Above: The cap of Hickling Mill being rebuilt. (August 1990)

Below: The boat-shaped cap of Hickling Mill being fitted with weatherboarding. (August 1990)

Above: The front of Hickling Mill cap with horizontal supports for the outside gallery. (August 1990)

Below: The cap of Hickling Mill seen from the top of the tower. (August 1990)

Restoration of the cap had been completed far enough by the end of October 1990 for it to be craned into position on Hickling Mill. (October 1990)

Above: The cap from Billingford Mill in course of restoration. (May 1990)

Left: The curb below the massive cap of Zeddam tower mill was made from wood with wooden teeth. The miller pulled the rope to turn the wooden reduction gearing. (March 1992)

Above: The winch wheel in the cap of a North Holland polder mill at Schermerhorn. (August 1990)

Above left: Tailpoles and winch on Herringfleet smock drainage mill, the last of its type in England. (March 1990)
Above right: The central tail pole is strengthen by braces on either side at Herringfleet Mill. (March 1990)
Right: The winch at the bottom of the tailpole at Herringfleet Mill. Part of the scoopwheel can be seen behind the boarding. (March 1990)

A typical capstan winch, here on one of the Kinderdyke polder mills. The rope for the brake is tied to the tailpole.

Below left: Operating the winch on Offellt Mill was hard work. Each row of bricks on the mill tower is set in a little to obtain the batter. (March 1992)
Below right: The tailpoles on the mill at Stavenisse, Tholen Island, have been fitted with a modern winch. The anchor posts are spaced at regular intervals around the mill. (August 1990)

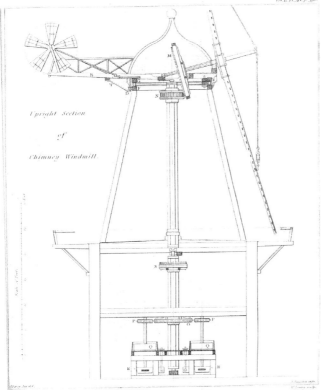

Above left: On mills with staging, such as De Kat at Zaandam, the tailpole had to be anchored to the staging itself. (August 990)

Above right: On tall powerful mills, such as De Valk, Leiden, the staging had to be very strong to secure the tailpole.

Left: John Smeaton's Drawing of the fantail for Chimney Mill, Newcastle-upon-Tyne, 1782. The fantail was probably too far behind the cap which may have caused the mill to yaw or swing backwards and forwards. Smeaton may have been uncertain of the strength of the cross on the windshaft because he fitted a forestay and ropes to the stocks.

Above left: The cap has been lifted onto Billingford Mill to the delight of birds. The mill was constructed in about 1862 to replace a post mill that was blown down when tail-winded. (May 1990)
Above right: The gearing and shafting from the fantail to the curb on Billingford Mill. (May 1990)
Below left: The fantail, gallery and petticoat on the cap of Upminster Mill. (May 1990)
Below right: Part of the gearing on Billingford Mill. (May 1990)

Above: The size of the fantail from Bardwell Mill is appreciated better when on the ground. (May 1990)

Right: The angle of the blades can be seen when mounted on the framing of Holton post mill. (May 1990)

Above left: Shafting and gearing from the fantail on Great Bircham Mill. (June 1990)

Above right: A six bladed fantail drives the carriage on Holton post mill. (May 1990)

Left: The six bladed fantail and carriage on the post mill at Aythorpe Roding. (May 1990)

Opposite page: The eight bladed fantail on Stanton post mill drives the wheels through the differential of a rear axle from a car. (May 1990)

Left: On some of the tall post mills in East Sussex, such as that at Hogg Hill, Icklesham, the fan was placed at the top of the buck, necessitating a long drive shaft to the wheels at the bottom of the carriage. The mill is reputed to have been built some two miles away at Pett at the end of the seventeenth century before being moved to its present site shortly before 1790.
(June 1967 or January 1968)

Below: The final drive to the carriage on the mill at Hogg Hill was through a worm gear which would have prevented the carriage from moving when the fan was not revolving.
(January 1968)

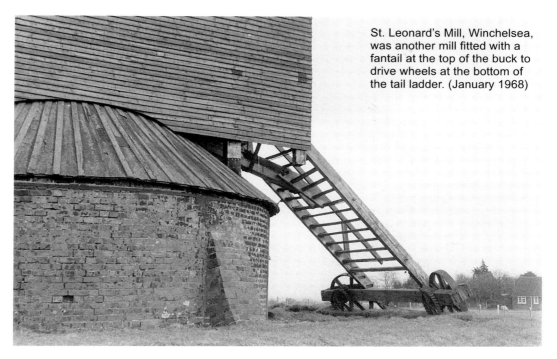

St. Leonard's Mill, Winchelsea, was another mill fitted with a fantail at the top of the buck to drive wheels at the bottom of the tail ladder. (January 1968)

Below left: The drive from the fantail could be disconnected to enable the miller to wind the cap by hand in emergency. Stow Mill, Paston, had such a link on the vertical shaft. (March 1990)
Below right: Cast iron external gearing on the curb on the top of the derelict Tunstall Bridge drainage mill. (June 1990)

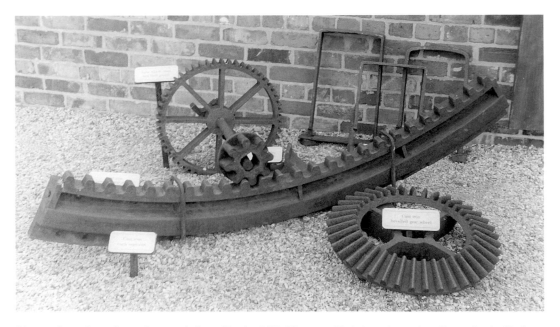

Above: A section of cast iron curb from Trader Mill, Sibsey, with internal gearing. It meshed with the pinion. (September 1990)
Below left: Typical Kentish cap, fantail and striking gear on Herne Mill. (April 1991)
Below right: The final drive to the curb on Charing Hill Mill was through a wooden worm gear under the cap. (March 1991)

Above left: The staging for the fly on Thaxted Mill was very short. The fly drove through a worm and external gear. The 'Y' wheel for operating the striking gear was well out to the right. (May 1990)

Above right: Fantail on Stracey Arms drainage mill with 'Y' wheel to operate the striking gear underneath.

Right: The drive from the fan on Swaffham Prior Mill was fitted with a crank which the miller could turn in emergency. (August 1995)

The present Swaffham Prior Mill replaced a post mill in 1860, ceasing to grind in 1950. The tower was built from brick, flint and clunch, a hard type of chalk. Fitted with four patent sails and a fantail, the mill would have needed little attention from the miller. (August 1995)

Above left: Caps on most mills were mounted on live curbs with rollers or trolley wheels to take the weight. The main bearing for the windshaft on Stones Mill, Halvergate Marshes, was carried on a pair of trolley wheels. (August 1990)

Above right: Guide or truck wheels might be fitted inside the curb to keep the cap central. This picture was taken looking up the tower of the derelict Stones Mill when most of the cap had rotted away. (August 1990)

Below: The top of the tower inside the White Mill, Sandwich, with wallower on the right and the curb and horizontal truck wheel in the centre, all made from wood. (March 1991)

The cap of Stow Mill, Paston, was mounted on a ring of rollers. The beam on the left carries the tail bearing for the cast iron windshaft seen above it. (March 1990)

The beam top left carries the tail bearing for the windshaft with the striking rod passing through it. The cap was mounted on well-spaced trolley wheels and located by horizontal truck wheels at Thelnetham Mill. (May 1990)

At Thelnetham Mill, the truck wheels ran in a channel to help prevent the cap being blown off. (May 1990)

Left: Cap of West Kingsdown Mill with brakewheel and pair of truck wheels bottom left. (May 1990)

Below: The internal gearing on the curb of Trader Mill, Sibsey, with truck wheels on the left and right and pinion drive in the centre. (September 1990)

8. Power Transmission

While the skill of the millwright is readily apparent in the structures of post and smock mills, it is less noticeable in the machinery inside. Here different problems had to be overcome through the need to transmit the torque for the sails down to the millstones or other moving parts. In early mills, nearly all this had to be constructed from wood for the cost of wrought iron was expensive even if it were available for the larger parts. Nowhere was this more difficult than with the windshaft. At its square outer end, it had to be pierced twice to take the pair of stocks, a very weak point. Then a neck had to be formed for the main bearing, the bearing itself most likely being a stone block. The square section continued through the brake wheel which would be the clasp arm variety. The rim was mounted on four arms which formed a square at the centre. Securing the brake wheel onto the square of the windshaft with wedges ensured accuracy of rotation. The tail end of the windshaft had an iron gudgeon driven into it for the back bearing.

The windshaft rests at an angle through the buck or cap. Various reasons have been given. One is that, on a tapering tower or smock mill, the main bearing is brought closer into the framing. Another is that, because wind speeds are slower at ground level due to obstructions, the wind does not blow horizontally but slightly downwards so an inclined shaft helps the sails to face the wind better. Then, as the brake wheel rotates and turns the wallower on top of the main vertical shaft to transmit the power, the two gears will be forced apart which is counteracted by the inclination of the windshaft. But the inclination makes the design of these gear wheels more difficult, particularly with later bevel wheels because they are not at right angles. Joining wooden shafts, such as a tall vertical shaft, was always difficult, hence the need to keep shafting as short as possible, which caused the millstones to be located near the top of the mill. The millwright had to know the best type of wood for each part, such as harder apple wood or hornbeam for the gear teeth which had to be mortised into the wheels.

Much of this changed with the introduction of cast iron during the second half of the eighteenth century. It was particularly advantageous for windshafts and their poll ends. While a cast iron poll end could be made much smaller, this material was not entirely suitable because it is weak in tension, and so was liable to crack when the stocks were wedged in. But it was far easier to make gear wheels and other parts from cast iron, although it was found best to have wooden teeth in one wheel running against cast iron in its mate. Bearing blocks could be cast in iron with brass or bronze bearing surfaces let in. While cast iron was an improvement over wood for shafting, the answer here was wrought iron which stood twisting and torque better as well as being lighter. Also the ends could be turned true for gudgeons which formed part of the shaft itself and were not an addition like those on wooden shafts.

There is no doubt that the introduction of iron during the nineteenth century transformed the interior mechanism of windmills, enabling the construction of the taller East Anglian mills. Also the spread across the country of patent sails and fantails owed much to the gearing, bearings and many small parts and shafts being made of cast or wrought iron.

Opposite page: The stocks must pass through two large holes carved into the poll end of a wooden shaft, seriously weakening it. The whips of Finchingfield post mill are fixed to the fronts of the stocks and the framing supported by back stays. (May 1990)

Above left: The cast iron poll end or canister of the windshaft on Billingford Mill. Since the stocks need to be set as close together near the main bearing as possible, the casting where they pass each other is quite thin and weak. (May 1990)

Above right: The massive cast iron poll end for Hickling Mill with the main bearing behind it. (May 1990)

Below: A newly cast windshaft for Bardwell Mill to replace the earlier one which had broken at the poll end. The shaft was cast hollow for lightness, hence the added section with the tail bearing at the right end. The brake wheel would be mounted on the two square plates near the centre. (May 1990)

Above: Cast iron windshaft and brake wheel from Cadges Mill, Reedham. The brake wheel has been cast in two halves with slots around the rim into which the gear teeth will be mortised. (August 1990)
Below left: Wawby post mill has a windshaft with a cast iron cross to which the ends of the stocks have been secured with clamps called bridle irons. (September 1990)
Below right: The advantage of the cast iron cross for multi-sailed mills can be seen in this example at Wymondham Mill. The mill also has a shapely ogee cap and finial. (July 1991)

Main bearing of the windshaft passing through the cap of West Kingsdown Mill. (May 1990)

Below left: Wood has been retained for the inner portion of the windshaft at Bourn Mill. The clasp-arm wooden brake wheel has been fitted with later cast iron toothed segments. The links on the ends of the band brake are on the right. (January 1974)

Below right: The clasp-arm gear wheels and shafting of Zeddam Mill are all wooden. The top bearing of the vertical shaft runs in a cross beam which is part of the cap. It is essential that this bearing remains central when the cap is turned around, otherwise the meshing of the brake wheel and wallower will be affected. (March 1992)

Left: At Het Prinsenhof, a cast iron windshaft has replaced an earlier wooden one. The original wooden brake wheel has been retained but wooden packing has had to be inserted to fill the gaps left by the removal of the much larger wooden shaft. The wallower in the bottom of the picture has vertical wooden peg teeth to engage with the near horizontal ones of the brake wheel. (March 1992)

Above: The links on the static end of a wooden brake band running against the circumference of a wooden brake wheel rim at Stow Mill, Paston. (March 1990)

Left: West Kingsdown Mill has a composite brake wheel with cast iron boss and spokes with wooden rim and wooden teeth. Round the outside are the large wooden brake blocks. (May 1990)

The brake wheel of Sutton Mill has been cast in two halves and fitted with wooden teeth. The band brake is composed of small blocks of wood, backed by iron banding. (June 1990)

The brake band of Wicklewood Mill is fitted on its own rim behind the gear teeth on the cast iron brake wheel. Many of the teeth are missing. The cracks between the weatherboarding have been filled to prevent rain penetration. (April 1985)

The cap of Wilton Mill has wrought iron spars to support the roof. The brake wheel is fitted with a steel brake band. (September 1990)

As well as operating the main sets of stones, power might be needed to drive auxiliary machinery such as sack hoists and flour graders. Here, in the top of Framsden post mill, the winch for the chain sack hoist would be worked by tensioning the flat belt on the pulley at the back. The belt would be driven by another pulley. (May 1990)

At Thelnetham Mill, the horizontal shaft was driven by bevel gearing from the main shaft. By raising the far end of the shaft, the belt would be tensioned to drive a device below. (May 1990)

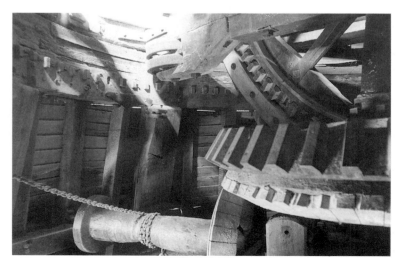

The sack hoist in West Kingsdown Mill has seen much use. It is driven off the wallower by the coned friction drive. (May 1990)

Right: At Sarre Mill, the flat pulley would be raised to be driven by the bottom ring of the wallower to rotate the sack hoist on the right. Dropping the pulley onto the lower beam would act as a brake. (April 1991)

Below; Bevel drive for a power take-off at Wilton Mill. (September 1990)

The wallower on the Cat & Fiddle post mill. Here the beam supporting the top bearing for the vertical shaft is fixed because the whole buck turns. The mill had been tail-winded, hence no windshaft. (June 1990)

Hickling Mill under restoration. The curb is being rebuilt. The cap will have to be located over the top of the gudgeon on the top of the vertical shaft. The lower set of teeth on the wallower drive the sack hoist to the left. (August 1990)

The top gudgeon of the vertical shaft at Sarre Mill is being kept in place by temporary staging from the new iron curb. The wallower is also a new casting. (April 1991)

Above left: Inside the cap of Thelnetham Mill with the inclined windshaft running across the top of the photograph with brake wheel on the right and wallower below. (May 1990)
Above right: The wallower with friction drive underneath and wooden vertical shaft at Great Thurlow smock mill. (May 1990)
Below: Wilton Mill has iron gearing and shafting. Beneath the wallower is a coned friction drive power take-off. (September 1990)

Above: The late date (1877) of Trader Mill, Sibsey, meant that it was fitted out with iron brake wheel, wallower and vertical shaft. There is a friction drive for the pulley wheel under the wallower. (September 1990)

Right: The iron vertical shaft was probably fitted to Heckington Mill when the eight sails were installed in 1892. (March 1990)

Below: The great spur wheel at the bottom of the vertical shaft of Bardwell Mill is supported on a massive curved wooden beam. (May 1990)

Above left: The vertical shaft of Hickling Mill with its cross-armed great spur wheel rests in a bridging box with bolts for accurate alignment. (August 1990)
Above right: The bottom end of the vertical shaft of Sutton Mill with its bridging box and alignment bolts. The bevel gears drive the governor in the background. (June 1990)
Below: Cross-armed great spur wheel and stone nut on a quant at the White Mill, Sandwich. The quant would be moved to one side out of the glut box to disengage the drive. (March 1991)

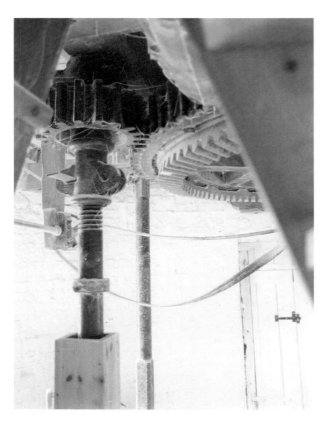

Left: The stone nut at Bardwell Mill could be disengaged by screwing it up. (May 1990)

Below: At West Kingsdown Mill, the stone nut could be engaged by lifting it up. (May 1990)

Above: At Sutton Mill, the stone nut was lowered onto a taper seating. (June 1990)

Right: Interior of Alford Mill showing the drive from the great spur wheel through the stone nut, down the quant to the runner stone. (July 1990)

9. Applications of Windmills

The windmill is a source of rotary power in which the amount of power generated and the speed of rotation depends upon availability of wind. But the wind is never constant. Therefore the most suitable applications of windmills are those where the time when the mill needs to be used is not that critical and where the quality of the product is not affected by variations in speed. These variations through the gusting of the wind will be smoothed out to a certain extent by the weight of the sails and transmission shafting acting as a sort of flywheel through their mass which gives a certain inertia to the system. This was certainly the case in milling corn which was the most popular and widespread employment of windmills. But even in this case, the miller was wise to make maximum use of any suitable wind. The last Pocklington at Heckington mill told me that, as a lad, he came home late one night after being out with his girlfriend. It had been a period of calm and he was surprised to find his father in overalls ready to go into the mill. 'Wind's rising, lad', his father said, 'Get changed', and he spent the rest of the night working in the mill. But, as the time factor became more critical in modern life and delivery dates loomed large, flour milling by wind had to yield to other more reliable forms of power.

After corn milling, the next important task for windmills has been raising water. Windmills to keep mines dry were probably used only as a last resort for fear of the mine being drowned out in a calm. Captain Trevithick's experience in Cornwall was rather different when the windmill he erected on Ding Dong mine sometimes went so fast that they could not stop it. But for pumping water for domestic supply, it was not critical when the mill operated provided there was adequate storage capacity to balance supply and demand. The numbers of the later American style windpumps in country areas serving farms is evidence of the potential of this form of power. Likewise in land drainage, the windmill could raise water that had been stored in the lower land drains.

As long as paper was made by hand, a windmill was adequate for driving either the early form of pulping machinery, cam or trip operated stampers, or the Dutch invention of the roll or Hollander beater. But the papermaking machines introduced soon after 1800 needed a more reliable source of power. While the Dutch had wind-powered fulling stocks for felting woollen cloth which were similar in principle to papermaking stampers, wind power was never successful for spinning machinery. Soon after 1790, Peter Ewart visited a cotton mill in Stockport turned by wind. He asked the manager what they did when they had no wind who replied, 'We play us'. No textile mill owner could afford to have hands standing idle. The conclusion has to be drawn that, while wind power was tried in a host of industries, for most purposes it was a marginal source of power through its unreliability and, with the exceptions of corn milling and water raising, its use in other industries quickly died out through competition from steam engines and later sources of power.

The equipment in these other wind-powered industries was developed mostly from a few basic types of machines. The horizontally rotating millstones might be adapted to grind mustard or pepper. Larger ones might hull barley or rice. Millstones set on edge, edge runners or kollergangs, crushed a wide variety of materials, such as dyestuffs and colours for paint; cole seed, linseed and rape seed for oil; flint for pottery; chalk for whiting or cement; as well as rags for papermaking. Then a mill might have a rotating camshaft to lift hammers or stampers for pounding more finely some of the materials mentioned above as well as preparing flax and fulling cloth. Other mills might prepare cocoa, spices, snuff, tobacco as well as much more. Most of these could once be found in the Zaan area of the Netherlands where there are favourable winds funnelled through the English Channel between the North Sea and the Atlantic.

It may have been improvements to the sails which stimulated the rise of the Dutch industrial windmill. The technology was linked to that of waterpower but had to be modified to suit the particular constraints of a cramped building that needed to present as small as possible an obstruction to the wind. Construction materials were most frequently wood, not only for the mills themselves but also for drainage works such as bridges, sluices and locks; for ships employed in the fishing industry and the merchanting trade; as well as for people's houses. These wooden industries were supplemented through the application of windpower to sawing. Cornelis Corneliszoon of Uitgeest patented a reciprocating saw driven by a sort of wipmolen in December 1593 with the saw out in the open. He greatly improved this by 1600, soon after which the 'Paltrok' sawmill appeared. Kollergangs with pairs of stones were possibly the subject of another patent by Cornelis Corneliszoon in 1597. Papermaking was introduced to the Netherlands at Alkmaar and Dordrecht in 1586 in mills perhaps operated by horsepower. The first windpowered mill in the Zaan area, the Goose, dates from 1605. Barley hulling followed in 1639. These are but a few instances of the industrial application of windpower in the Netherlands during the opening years of the seventeenth century where the industrial mill became a common feature of the landscape in the north-western regions. Yet in England the numbers of industrial mills remained small, probably through the lesser strength of the winds in the eastern part of the country while further west, waterpower was more readily available.

10. Corn Milling

Corn milling is the application which most people associate with windmills. The common hand quern was adapted first for watermills and then transferred to windmills. The quern consisted of a circular stationary bedstone with a flat upper surface on top of which the runner stone was rotated by hand. The runner has a hole or eye in its centre through which grain was dribbled by hand. The surfaces of the stones might be grooved the better to grind the corn as well as assisting the flour to emerge round the circumference.

The millstones in Persian windmills which survived into the 1970s were carved out of hard grit and were nearly five feet in diameter. The bedstone rose slightly towards the centre while the runner was dished to marry with it. The eye and the skirt were pot-marked to draw the wheat in and expel it as well as to break it up. The middle or breast was left smooth so that the flour would become finer. The runner rotated up to a maximum of 30 r.p.m. so grinding was a slow process, restricted to a few grains at a time. At such speeds, little heat was generated. A runner leaning against the Xaghra Mill in Gozo is also smooth, indicating a similar slow process. Runners in England would rotate at between 50 and 140 r.p.m. with stones about 4 ft. 6 ins. diameter but in practice the mill is regulated to about 120 r.p.m. to prevent the flour overheating. When a mill is grinding, the flour will give off a nice warm smell.

The bedstone must be set horizontal in the floor in which there will be a slot to allow the flour to pass down the spout into a sack or meal bin. A spindle passes through a hole in the centre of the bedstone which must have a seal to prevent grain falling through. The bottom of the spindle rests in a thrust bearing mounted in a bridge box which is adjustable for horizontal alignment. This box is supported on the bridge tree, pivoted at one end with a fine vertical adjustment at the other. It is this tenter mechanism which controls the gap between the stones and hence the fineness of the flour.

In England, there were two types of stones in general use. For coarser work, latterly animal feed, Peaks or greys would be used. These were quarried in a single piece from millstone grit in Derbyshire. For finer flour, composite stones were assembled from very hard French burr. Quarried in the Paris basin, this type of stone occurs naturally only in small pieces. Therefore the millstone had to be made up of precision-dressed blocks, cemented together with iron bands shrunk on around them. The non-working surface was smoothed over with plaster of Paris. French burr was imported in lumps and made up in this country.

On top of the spindle is fitted the mace which, in turn, carries the rhynd. The rhynd is a metal arch, the ends of which carry the runner so it is balanced on top of the mace and spindle. This spindle is driven from the great spur wheel at the lower end of the vertical shaft. When the gearing is underneath the stone floor, it is termed underdrift. More usually in a windmill, the rhynd is driven from above, overdrift, by a rod called a quant. In both cases, the final drive to the spindle or quant is through a stone nut which can be engaged or disengaged with the great spur wheel.

In the later tall nineteenth century mills, the top floor would contain storage bins from which the grain would fall down a shute into the hopper of a set of stones. Otherwise the miller emptied the sack directly into the hopper. The hopper is mounted on a wooden framing, the horse, which in turn is supported by the wooden casing surrounding the stones, sometimes called the tun or vat. Below the hopper is the shoe, a tapering sloping trough which ends above the eye of the runner. The grain runs down the slope, aided by vibration from the damsel. The damsel may be a square part of the quant or fashioned from three or four rods. The shoe is held against it by a spring so its shaking keeps the grain running down smoothly. It makes a continual chattering, hence the name. The rate of feed can be regulated by changing the inclination of the shoe.

For the best flour, the grains should not be crushed but cut. Therefore in northern Europe the millstones were dressed after patterns found in Roman querns. First, the working surface is made flat, checked by a straight edge called a paint staff because it is smeared with red raddle which leaves a mark on the high spots. Wedge-shaped sections called harps are marked out and a groove or furrow cut along the radius of one side. One side of this furrow, the breast, is vertical and forms the cutting edge, while the other side, the skirt, slopes back up to the surface. Further furrows are cut in the harp, leaving lands between them. Patterns thus formed vary but the runner and bedstone have to be identical so that when the runner is placed upside down on top, the breasts cross each other in a sort of scissors action. The flour passes out round the circumference of the stones inside the casing and is swept down the spout. French burr stones might be dressed every fortnight if used regularly, a slow tedious task with a steel bill held in a wooden thrift.

The quality of the flour depends upon the gap between the runner and bedstone. So not only does the runner have to be balanced accurately to run true, but the bridge tree supporting it has to be raised or lowered according to speed. An increase in speed causes the runner to rise and coarsen the meal. The miller would test the meal falling down the spout and alter the tenter setting accordingly. A gusty wind would require his full attention to this task. Starting in the 1780s, centrifugal governors began to be introduced. They did not control the speed of the mill since their speed was directly linked to that of the stones. An increase in speed caused their weights to rise which would counteract the rise of the runner through levers linked to the bridge tree. This movement could be in the order of 1/100 of an inch or so.

The meal coming from the stones would be 80% flour and 20% bran. Demand in the nineteenth century for better quality flour led to the introduction of bolters or dressers in which the bran could be sifted out and the flour graded. These machines would be situated in the lower floor of the mill and required additional power to work them. In a gentle breeze of 5 m.p.h. or so, a mill runs very slowly, producing half a hundred weight of flour an hour. As the wind increases up to 20 m.p.h., two pairs of stones may be run each of which will mill up to four hundred weight of flour an hour.

The millstone outside the Xaghra Mill in Gozo has a flat surface with no dressing so probably rotated quite slowly.
(April 1996)

The millstone in the Xaghra Mill almost fills the milling chamber. The shoe is vibrated by the stick rubbing on the upper surface of the runner to regulate the speed. The casing barely covers the sides. (April 1996)

Above: A grey runner stone in Cross-in-Hand post mill ready dressed with the slot for the rhynd in the eye, showing the furrows cut between the lands. (May 1990)

Left: Grey runner with rhynd in position and broken quant at Heckington Mill. (March 1990)

Above left: A different method of dressing a grey runner at Wicklewood Mill. (April 1985)

Above right: A pair of French burrs at Stow Mill, Paston, formed from many lumps. The bedstone is on the right and the runner on the left. (March 1990)

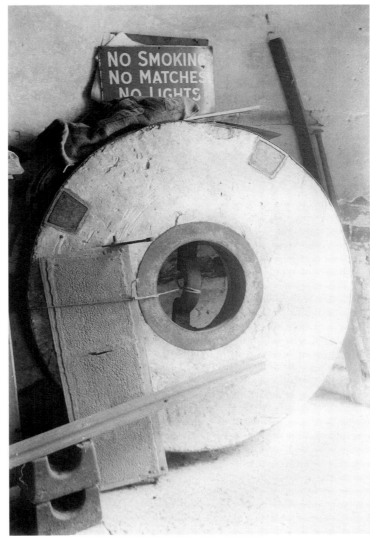

Right: The plastered surface of a French burr runner with pockets at the circumference for balance weights in Framsden post mill. These stones needed to be banded to prevent disintegration when running. (May 1990)

Above left: The casing and runner have been removed at Dobson's Mill, Burgh-le-Marsh. The quant drives the runner from above, overdrift, but the rhynd has been removed and placed on the casing. The weight of the runner was taken by the spindle passing through the bedstone. (August 1990)

Above right: There was little space to spare in Bourn post mill. The windshaft passes close to the top of the overdrift quant which has been disengaged from the glut box. The hopper is on the left with the shoe sloping down to the eye. A wooden casing covers the stones. The damsel is made from rods. (January 1974)

Left: The smart casing round the overdrift stones at Bardwell Mill. A thrift with bill for dressing the stones lies on top. The hopper is supported by the horse. The shoe underneath is vibrated by the square portion of the quant and is held against it by the rope from the wooden spring. When the hopper is nearly empty the bell will ring. (May 1990)

Above left: This pair of stones in Heckington Mill is driven from the great spur wheel above. The hopper can be fed from the storage bins on an upper floor down a shute. The hopper is mounted on the horse over the casing. (March 1990)

Above right: The supports for the horse at Skidby Mill have been turned in a lathe. The angle of the overdrift quant shows that the stone nut has been disengaged from the great spur wheel above. The iron vertical shaft is in the foreground. (July 1990)

Right: The stones at Thelnetham Mill were underdrift, driven from below, giving easier access from above with no heavy quant. The damsel is made from four rods which hit the side of the shoe tensioned by the string and wooden slat spring. The string from the bell is attached to a strip of leather which is held down in the hopper by the weight of the grain. When nearly empty, this is freed, allowing the bell to be struck by the damsel and warn the miller. (May 1990)

Above: The underdrift stones at Great Thurlow smock mill have been fitted with a tentering device to regulate the gap between them. (May 1990)

Below: A view across the cramped milling chamber in Sutton Mill with four underdrift sets of stones. Those on the left foreground are French burrs with their strengthening bands. (June 1990)

Great Bircham Mill was fitted with a crane to lift the runner stone. (June 1990)

The gap between the runner and bedstones was determined by raising or lowering one end of the bridge tree on which was mounted the bridging box to support the spindle below the runner. Centrifugal governors were fitted after the 1780s to control this gap automatically as seen here at Bourn Mill. A pulley has been fitted to the bottom of the stone spindle round which the broken flat belt would pass to the pulley at the top of the governor. The weights would fly out when rotated, raising the end of the bent lever to adjust the gap. (January 1974)

The governor at the White Mill, Sandwich, with driving belt in position. The weights are an unusual shape. (March 1990)

The governor at West Kingsdown Mill, long out of use. (May 1990)

Alford Mill had only one governor which was connected to three sets of stones through the horizontal bars on the left. A cast iron bridge tree is in the background.
(July 1990)

The governor and iron bridge tree below a set of stones at Heckington Mill in June 1968. The lag governor is a type where the weights move upwards in the same circle as they are suspended and not outwards.
(June 1968)

The same governor at Heckington Mill in 1990 guarded for health and safety reasons.
(March 1990)

Above left: The lag governor at Bardwell Mill with complex links to the bridge trees. (May 1990)
Above right: On the governor at Wymondham Mill, centrifugal force sends the weights sliding out along the horizontal bar which is caused to rise and so tenter the stones. (July 1991)

Below: The tentering mechanism of Trader Mill, Sibsey, can be manually adjusted as well as controlled by the governor. To the left of the adjusting mechanism, a wooden meal spout takes the flour down to the sacks. (September 1990)

Horizontal dressing machine for taking bran out of the flour in the round house at Saxted Green post mill. (May 1990)

The inclined flour dresser or wire machine at the White Mill, Sandwich, was fed from the stone floor to separate the bran and grade the flour. Internal rotating brushes brushed the meal against progressively coarser gauze in the drum, the finest quality passing out at the top end with the final waste trailing out at the bottom. (March 1991)

Inclined flour dresser at Wilton Mill. (September 1990)

11. Water Pumping

Windmills were used for pumping water out of mines or quarries in many parts of the country as well as the one mentioned already in Cornwall. In 1700, one was erected at Wroxall on the Somerset coalfield. Ruins of towers exist in Fife on that coalfield, dating from a similar period. A contemporary illustration of one of these shows a long vertical shaft driving a horizontal camshaft at the bottom of the mill which operated a pair of lever pumps. One of the slate quarries in the Nantlle Valley, North Wales, tried a windmill some years later, in this case to supplement waterpower. But the unreliability of the wind meant that their use was very restricted and only ruins survive.

Above: Perhaps the most dramatic pumping windmill relic is the ruined tower on top of the desolate wastes of the copper mines on Parys mountain in Anglesey. This five sailed mill was built in 1878 to assist an existing steam engine. Its main shaft turned a crankshaft at the bottom of the mill through a bevel gear. Two hundred feet of reciprocating wooden rods linked the mill to the steam engine, effecting a considerable saving of coal, all of which had to be carted to the top of the mountain. While still working in 1901, it had ceased by 1910. (August 1991)

Left: Little windmill pumps were once common around the coast at salt works, gravel and sand pits. A couple of dozen brickworks used windpumps in the basin of the Yorkshire Ouse. One surviving example is at the claypits for the brickyard at Elvington. The brick tower has four common sails and a cranked windshaft directly connected to a single-acting bucket pump. (April 2005)

Left: Elvington. The crank on the windshaft is in the vertical position with the thin connecting rod running down the centre of the mill. (April 2005)

Right: The hollow post mill at Starston near Harleston was built around 1850 to pump water from the river for irrigation purposes. The eight foot diameter round house supports an iron column down which the pump rod passes. Four spring sails are winded by a pair of tail vanes so it would have functioned almost without attention. (May 1990)

Above: Close up of the 'buck' on the Starston windpump. It was winded by the tail vanes. (May 1990)

Below: A sail on the Starston wind pump with wire-framed shutters falling into disrepair. (May 1990)

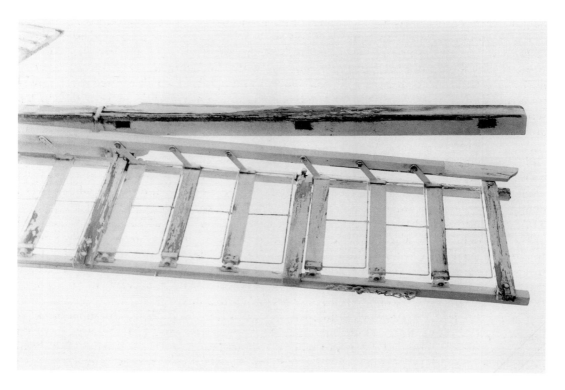

12. Land Drainage Mills

Necessity is the mother of invention. Deteriorating conditions in the flat polder lands of the Netherlands compelled the people living there to seek for more powerful machines to raise the water out of the lands they had laboured to wrest from the clutches of sea and river inundations. The greater part of the Netherlands consists of a delta area formed from alluvial deposits brought down the rivers including the Maas, Rhine and Waal. When people began to inhabit this region, they built islands from the local clay on which they could live. The first dam in a river for protection against high tides was erected in A.D. 802. Cultivation for wheat started around A.D. 1,000 on land drained by digging ditches to carry off the water. However conditions deteriorated, caused by shrinkage of the silt and peat areas. After a severe flood in 1134, the first systematic collective defence against flooding was developed in the south western part of Netherlands. The concept of surrounding an area with a bank and digging drainage channels leading to sluices in the banks was adopted rapidly elsewhere. Much of this land drained naturally since it was above the level of low tides but resort also had to be made to artificial means.

To begin with, men or animals were the only power available for raising water. Men used buckets or ladles or scoops to hurry the water along the ditches and throw it over the banks. But soon these methods proved inadequate, particularly for larger areas. Some genius realised that a waterwheel which create power through water striking its blades and so turning it round could be reversed. If rotated by some source of power in the opposite direction, it could be converted into a scoopwheel in which water was raised by the ladles or scoops around its rim. The first definite mention of one does not occur until 1441 but it is assumed that this was the water-raising device operated by the first windmills. Lift pumps such as those used in mines could have been employed but these are more suited for raising a little water to a great height rather than a lot of water to a low height. Also scoopwheels had no valves which might be blocked by reeds or other debris.

The technology for a scoopwheel existed not only in the form of a waterwheel but also in both wind and water-powered corn mills where the power source drove the runner stone through gearing and shafting. Compared with the layout in a wind-powered corn mill, the gear ratios needed to be altered to drive a scoopwheel which rotated more slowly than the sails. The vertical shaft had to be extended to engage with the pitwheel on the scoopwheel axle in the bottom of the mill. While some forms of waterwheel might operate more or less in the open such as those on boat-mills with the water flowing around them, the scoopwheel must be contained within a close-fitting structure forming sides and a curving breast to prevent the water running back into the drain. This structure could also support the bearings of the horizontal axle running through the middle of the wheel as well as the pitwheel needed to drive it. The ladles or scoops of the wheel had to be inclined to prevent the water, as it was being lifted, from running back over their tops. This also limited the lift or height to which the water could be raised to about one third of the diameter of the wheel. While this slope of the ladles helped the water to run off at the higher level, they entered the water in the drain too nearly horizontal so did not dip in cleanly. Also there could be considerable churning of the water at the exit which wasted energy. At the exit, self-closing sluice doors were fitted to prevent the river water running back into the drain when the mill was not working.

The earliest land drainage windmills were most likely tower mills adapted from existing examples of corn mills. These had made their appearance by 1400. But we have seen that the lighter, cheaper structures of wooden wipmolens and smock mills were utilised during the fifteenth century. (See p30) The Dutch example was followed in the English

Fens during the sixteenth century. Certainly by the 1580s, there were several wind-powered drainage mills on the silt lands around Fosdyke and Crowland. The history of windmills used to drain the Fens has been covered in my *Machines, Mills and Uncountable Costly Necessities*, republished recently with additional material as *The Drainage of the Fens*. Therefore this will not be repeated here. Also the only significant surviving windmill in the Fens is the little one now preserved in Wicken Fen which is occasionally used to pump water into the Fen. It was built originally in 1908 as a skeleton mill to drain 30 acres of the near-by Adventurers Fen. The weatherboarding was added a couple of years later. I have continued to use the term windmill and not wind-pump for drainage mills fitted with traditional sails to distinguish them from wind-pumps fitted with the American style multi-bladed rotors.

Wind-powered drainage mills soon caused the problem of land shrinkage to reappear. This is a great hazard with peat because bacteriological action, which starts as the peat is dried, causes the peat to be eaten away so that the land level falls. The difference in height between the drain and the river became greater than a wind-powered scoopwheel could manage. So in the seventeenth century, the Dutch introduced the water-raising device invented by the Greek Archimedes, his screw. It had a great advantage over scoopwheels where a high lift was required. The screw was assembled from wooden segments fixed around an inclined wooden shaft. Sometimes these were covered with boarding to form a tube but more generally open screws ran in brick troughs. The lower bearing would be immersed in the drainage channel so the blades of the screw dipped into the water. The bevel driving gear at the upper end had to have suitable angles to cope with the inclination of the shaft.

But peat particularly might shrink so much that the lift became beyond the scope even of an Archimedes screw. Then one mill might lift the water into a storage pond from where it was raised by a second to the river in the double-lift system. This was resorted to sometimes in the Fens such as at Nordelph where the bases of two tower mills still survive. Where two mills failed to cope, the triple-lift arrangement had to be introduced with three mills and two storage ponds, the second higher than the first. Both methods failed when one mill broke down. So in the Netherlands, a system of ring canals was adopted in some of the large polders. An appropriate number of mills raised the water into a common ring canal from where a second group lifted it again to the river. The rest of the mills could continue working in the event of one stopping.

In England, many drainage windmills have survived in the Norfolk Broads area where such machines seem to have been installed much later than the Fens. This could have been due to the different types of agriculture practised. The Fens concentrated more and more on arable cultivation to supply the growing Midland and northern towns of the Industrial Revolution. The Norfolk Broads were better placed to produce fodder and bedding for the numerous horses in the ever-expanding metropolis of London. Records of dates for construction of drainage mills on the Broads do not start until the middle of the eighteenth century. The one built into the gateway of St. Benet's Abbey is the oldest with a date of 1735 – 40, but it was used first for crushing cole seed for oil. Wiseman Mill, at Ashby on the Bure, has a date of 1753 and Brograve Mill, Walcot Marsh near Sea Palling, 1771. All these had brick towers. Building continued apace throughout the nineteenth century and even into the twentieth. The mill at Horsey Mere was rebuilt in 1897 and again in 1912. Martham has a plate on the exterior which reads, 'Erected 1908', while another plate inside is inscribed, '1912 by England of Ludham'. One of the last mills to work under wind, Ashtree Farm near Great Yarmouth, was built in 1912 by Smithdales, the millwrights of Acle. It was tail-winded in 1953 and has since declined into a sorry wreck. A survey carried out in 1950 reached a total of 107 mills but there may have been as many as 140 in all. Their continued survival and use was undoubtedly due to the better wind regime here than in the Fens but it did not equal that in the Netherlands.

The last major innovation in land drainage mills was the introduction of turbine or centrifugal pumps to replace scoopwheels. J.G. Appold's centrifugal pump amazed the crowds visiting the 1851 Great Exhibition in Hyde Park. They could not understand how the 12 ins. diameter high speed rotor could lift 1,800 gallons of water 10 ft. high per minute. Another driven by a steam engine successfully drained Whittlesey Mere in the Fens later that year and proved that rotary pumps could be used successfully for land drainage. However arguments about the merits of scoopwheels or rotary pumps continued for many years. For windmills, rotary pumps had an advantage that they could be started more easily in light winds. Also a factor, not so critical in the Broads area compared with the Fens, was that they did not need the massive trough of a scoopwheel and so could be lowered more easily when the land shrank. Their initial and later maintenance costs were probably less than scoopwheels so that many were installed in windmills around the Broads and even some in the Netherlands.

Dutch
Drainage Mills

There were many small field mills in the Netherlands to improve the drainage of a small area. This example is preserved in the Zaan mill museum. (August 1990)

Above left: A little field mill preserved in the Arnhem Open Air Museum. (June 1972)

Above right: This little mill with octagonal base at Franeken in Friesland has unusual sails for the Netherlands. (August 1990)

Right: A fine example of a wipmolen with covered scoopwheel near Leiden. (May 1983)

Right: The exposed scoopwheel at the
Hellouw wipmolen. (March 1992)

Below: In a strong wind, spray from the
scoopwheel may be flung everywhere
creating a spectacular sight. Should the
wheel revolve too quickly, the ladles may
not be filled properly so the mill will
overspeed and run away. (March 1992)

The De Vrouw Venner
wipmolen was built in 1813. In
such mill, the buck may sway
alarmingly when working in
strong winds. (March 1992)

Above: A wipmolen among the
polder mills at Kinderdyke.
(May 1977)

Right: The thatched polder mill, the
Blauw or Blue Mill, has a boat-winch
beside it. (March 1992)

Below: The unusual twelve-sided
brick mill, the Rijpwetering, in the
Netherlands. (March 1992)

Above: The largest surviving concentration of drainage mills in the Netherlands is at Kinderdyke. The size of two polders here, the Overwaard and the Nederwaard, was too great for a single mill in each. As the lift through which the water had to be raised was not all that high, each polder had a row of mills lifting the water up to its own canal which formed storage basins from where it could be run off into the tidal river. This mill under full sail is one of the row of brick mills built in 1738. (May 1977)

Below: Some of the brick mills at Kinderdyke. (May 1977)

In 1740, thatched smock mills were built to drain the second polder at Kinderdyke. (May 1977)

A row of five thatched mills at Kinderdyke with the higher storage canals in the foreground. (May 1977)

Eleven mills can be seen here at Kinderdyke with their storage canals. On the left is a buck of a wipmolen. (May 1977)

The Archimedes Screw

Above: The shaft for an Archimedes screw with the helix cut in it at the Schermer polder. (April 1994)

Below:A complete triple-start Archimedes screw at the Arnhem Open Air Museum. Forming the blades of the screw was a neat piece of millwrighting. (June 1972)

Above left: An inside winding thatched polder mill at Schermer polder with internal Archimedes screw. The sails were turning gently with no cloth set. The brake lever projects from the rear of the cab.(August 1990)

Above right: The polder mill in the Arnhem Open Air Museum follows the practice of South Holland, being winded by tailpoles. It also has an internal Archimedes screw. (June 1972)

Below: A most unusual type of windmill had evolved before 1580 in the Friesian part of the Netherlands to operate an Archimedes screw. It was called the Tjasker. It had four common sails and brake fitted onto the upper end of the shaft for the screw. The bearing for the lower end of the enclosed screw was in the middle of a basin into which the water to be drained entered through a tunnel. The upper end was supported by a wheeled 'A' frame just behind the sails. To make the sails face the wind, the frame could be pushed round a circular track. This meant that the water from the screw outlet had to fall into a circular ditch as well. One Tjasker is perseveved in the Arnhem Open Air Museum.
(June 1972)

Above: Modern Archimedes screws at Kinderdyke. (May 1977)

Left: Modern Archimedes screws at Mautby Marsh, Norfolk. They have the advantage of being simple and are not clogged by reeds or other debris. (March 1990)

Multiple-Lift Mills

Above: A pair of double-lift mills in the Schermerhorn. The lower one on the left raises the water to the canal in the centre while the one on the right raises it through the main dyke bank. The right-hand mill is working while the left is not. (August 1990)

Right; The triple-lift mills in the Schermer polder are the North Holland inside winding type, operating internal Archimedes screws. (August 1990)

Above: A broken poll end from one of the mills in the Schermer polder. The cast iron windshaft has correctly curved ribs to give maximum strength with minimum material. The end of a steel stock lies in the background. (August 1990)

Right: One of the triple-lift mills in the Aarlanderveen polder. The sails are fitted with curved leading boards for greater efficiency. (March 1992)

Below: The row of triple-lift mills in Tweemans polder with storage ponds between them. (March 1992)

The tailpoles of one mill in the Aarlanderveen polder with a second mill in the background. In 1994, the Provincial Government of the Province of Zuid-Holland decided that the mills of this polder would remain as the principal means of drainage, making it the last polder in the Netherlands to rely on wind power. (March 1992)

Norfolk Broads
Drainage Windmills with Scoopwheels

Above: Herringfleet Mill on the River Waveney is a remarkable survival of the traditional smock mills once common on the Broads as well as in the Fens. It was built around 1825 and was kept at work by the Somerleyton Estate until 1956 or 1958. The corrugated iron building in the background houses the Ruston diesel engine for driving a turbine pump. (March 1990)

Left: Herringfleet Mill viewed from the river bank with the exit channel in the foreground. The cap has two tie-beams to which are joined the braces for the tailpole. (March 1990)

Below: The angle of the ladles on the scoopwheel of Herringfleet Mill is revealed with the covers removed. (March 1990)

Above left: The replacement turbine pump at Herringfleet Mill is minute compared with the scoopwheel. (March 1990)

Above right: The narrow wooden tower of St. Olaves windmill on the River Waveney was built in 1910 by Englands, the Ludham millwrights. The scoopwheel is under the housing with pitched roof. (March 1990)

Right: In spite of its small size, the St. Olaves windmill was equipped with patent sails with striking gear and fantail so it could have been left to run with only the minimum of attention. (March 1990)

Above left: The front tie-beam on the cap of High's Mill, Halvergate marshes, reminds us that the early Norfolk drainage mills would have been winded with tailpoles. The cap has been clad with aluminium as a temporary measure to preserve it. (August 1990)

Above right: In their isolated positions out on the marshes, mills such as this one at Six Mile House on the Bure quickly deteriorate without constant attention. It was fitted with patent sails and outside scoopwheel. (March 1990)

Below: Inside the base of Six Mile House Mill with the bottom of the vertical shaft and the pitwheel for driving the scoopwheel on the right. The great spur wheel on the left may have come from a corn mill. (March 1990)

Above left: The larger pitwheel on the shaft of the scoopwheel inside the base of Six Mile House Mill. The scoopwheel should rotate at three to four revolutions, or considerably slower than the sails. (March 1990)

Above right: Lockgate Mill, Breydon North Wall, is a medium size mill, now with cap protected temporarily with aluminium cladding. The machinery inside is complete except for the poll end. (March 1990)

Below: The scoopwheel at Lockgate mill is 19 ft. overall diameter, with ladles fitted onto a single cast iron framing. (March 1990)

Above left: A new cap and fantail were fitted to Howard's Mill, Halvergate marshes, in October 1989. This tarred brick mill stands 32 ft. high to the curb. (August 1990)
Above right: The scoopwheel of Howard's Mill was built with two pairs of castings. (August 1990)
Below: The scoopwheel boss and bearing at Howard's Mill. (August 1990)

Above left: View along the drain at Upper Four Mile Mill on the Bure. (March 1990)

Above right: The double-framed scoopwheel at Upper Four Mile Mill on the Bure. (March 1990)

Right: Restoration started on Mutton's or Manor Farm Mill, Halvergate marshes, in 1975. In 1990, only the sails remain to be fitted. (March 1990)

Left: The scoopwheel at Mutton's Mill was inside the tower. (March 1990)

Below: Berney Arms Mill was built in about 1869 to grind cement clinker obtained from the calcareous mud dredged up from the River Yare. The seven storey mill is over 70 ft. high and was built by Stolworthy's, millwrights of Great Yarmouth. The span of the patent sails is about 70 ft. Until the cement works closed around 1880, the mill drove edge runners but then it was converted to drive an external scoopwheel 24 ft. diameter 11 ins. wide. (August 1990)

Left: The patent sails on Berney Arms Mill. (March 1990)

Berney Arms Mill is now in the care of English Heritage, hence the cash desk opposite the gearing at the bottom of the vertical shaft. (August 1990)

The scoopwheel at Berney Arms Mill has an internal gear on the circumference of the scoopwheel casting. The drive-shaft from the mill is on the left. (March 1990)

Berney Arms Mill must be the only windmill to have its own railway station, but access is easier by boat. (March 1990)

Left: A single cylinder steam engine was installed in a shed by Polkey's Mill, Reedham. This view was taken in the 1930s when both Polkey's and Cadge's Mill in the background were fully operable. (Reid Collection)

Below: Polkey's Mill may be restored and has survived better that the steam engine which has been scrapped and that building is now completely derelict. (August 1990)

The pump at Horsey Mill is housed in the boarded box on the left. Rebuilt in 1898 and again in 1912, the mill ceased work in 1943 when struck by lightning. Now owned by the National Trust, it lost the fantail during a storm in 1987 but could not be worked anyway because the patent sails had no shutters. (August 1990)

Above: The equivalent of the great spur wheel at Horsey Mill drives a smaller pinion to increase the speed of the turbine pump. (August 1990)

Left: Stracey Arms Mill stands prominently beside the Norwich to Great Yarmouth road. Built in 1883, it has been kept in good repair by the Norfolk Windmill Trust since 1965. Because these mills can no longer be used for pumping, the shutters have been removed from the patent sails to prevent overspeeding. This view shows the outlet sluice with the pump casing on the left. (March 1990).

Above: The gearing in the cap of Stracey Arms Mill. (August 1990)

Right: The outfall sluice at Stracey Arms Mill with pump casing behind. (March 1990)

Below: The bottom of the vertical shaft at Stracey Arms Mill with the bevel gearing to drive the pump. (August 1990)

Left: When built in 1820, Thurne Dyke or Morse's Mill would have consisted of only the coned part of the tower. The tower would have been extended when a rotary pump, patent sails and fantail were added. It worked for nearly 120 years and was restored in the 1950s so that its white painted tower stands out prominently across the marshes. (March 1990)

Left: The inlet from the drain to the pump on Thurne Dyke Mill. (March 1990)

Above: Gearing for the rotary pump of Thurne Dyke Mill. (March 1990)

Above left: Perry's or Runham Swim Mill with gear drive to rotary pump. (March 1990)

Above right: The gear drive and casing of Runham Swim Mill. (March 1990)

Right: The date stone on Brograve Mill records 'BB 1771'. It was built by Sir Barney Brograve who is said to have hidden from the devil in it. Modernised with an internal rotary pump, patent sails and fantail, it has been derelict since well before the 1950s. The tower has little batter. (August 1990)

Above left: Inside of the Tunstall Dyke smock mill showing cant posts and bracing. (June 1990)

Above right: Remains of a rare smock mill on the Broads at Tunstall Dyke near Acle. It had an internal rotary pump.
(June 1990)

Right: The open trestle Boardman's Mill at How Hill on the River Ant photographed in 1969 before later restoration with cap, patent sails and eight-bladed fantail. (April 1969)

13. Industrial Mills

There was a remarkable combination in the Netherlands of good communication links with the interior of the Continent along the river systems as well as harbours at the mouths of these rivers where a maritime trade developed together with a favourable wind regime. All this gave rise to the adaptation of wind power to a great variety of industries. Although other countries followed this example and established industrial mills, it was the Netherlands where such mills remained viable economically longest and where a few examples of these sort of massive dinosaurs preserved in working order can be seen today. The mill which perhaps stimulated the Dutch economy most was the sawmill because wood formed the basis for the major part of anything constructed in the seventeenth century and timber sawn by windmills saved an immense amount of toil by hand sawyers. Therefore this section on industrial windmills starts with sawmills.

Sawmills

Above left: The paltrok, De Gekroonde Poelenburg, at Zaan. The whole mill turns on its broad brick base. The miller stands on the front staging and is preparing to set the sails. The panelling either side prevents the wind blowing across the sawing area and gives the name to this type of mill from its wide skirts. (March 1992)

Above right: De Gekroonde Poelenburg from the rear. (August 1990)

Left: The brake wheel on the windshaft turns a horizontal crankshaft which drives the reciprocating sawing frames below directly by long connecting rods. (August 1990)

Below: Rear view of the De Gekroonde Poelenburg showing the wide sawing platform with capstan winch in foreground. The mill turns on a roller race on top of the brick foundation. (August 1990)

Left: Turning the capstan winch on De Gekroonde Poelenburg to wind the mill needed great strength and weight. (March 1992)

Above left: The crane on De Gekroonde Poelenburg for hauling the tree trunks out of the canal where they will have been stored. (March 1992). Above right: The moving trolley on which the trunks are secured at the paltrok in the Arnhem Open Air Museum. There are no blades in the vertical sawing frame. (June 1972). Below: The ratchet mechanism for advancing the trolley on De Gekroonde Poelenburg. (March 1992)

Left: The saw frames with their sets of blades for cutting thin wainscot on De Gekroonde Poelenburg. (March 1992)

Right: The later type of much larger smock sawmill near Leiden. Only the cap turns. The sawing frames are situated in the centre of the mill so that the sawing area is completely enclosed under the extensions on either side. (May 1983)

Left: D'Heesterboom Mill at Leiden is another powerful sawmill which was built in 1804. The trunks would be drawn up from the canal through the end doors. (March 1992)

Above Left: The Agneta sawmill at Ruurle has a brick tower and a pair of modern self-reefing sails but is still winded with tailpoles. (March 1992)
Above right: Blackdown Mill at Punnett's Town, Sussex, was moved to its present position in 1856 to replace a post mill which burnt down. For a short time, it was run in conjunction with a sawmill. There were few wind-powered sawmills in Britain, principally owing to opposition from sawyers who destroyed one in London. (May 1990)

Mustard Mill

Right: The mustard mill, De Huiseman, on top of its warehouse in the Zaan museum area. (June 1972)

Barley Hulling Mill

Above: The powerful barley hulling mill, Het Prinsenhof in West Zaan, with warehouse and 'convenience' by canal. Hulled barley, such as pearl barley, is still used in some soups or stews.
(March 1992)

Middle: Inside Het Prinsenhof with great spur wheel on the right and lantern gear on the left to drive a quant for the hulling runner.
(March 1992)

Bottom: Storage bins and on the left the cover for the hulling stones in Het Prinsenhof. The barley would be dropped down the funnel. After polishing, the left-hand gate board would be raised to let the barley drop into bins on the lower floor.
(March 1992)

Right: The bottom surface of a barley hulling runner. The runner had only a few wide deep furrows through which the grains were flung without being ground. The walls of the casing were lined with tin sheeting in which holes had been beaten with sharp points turned inwards to form a cylindrical grater against which the grains were flung and rubbed. Barley hulling stones rotated faster than ordinary millstones, requiring a large, powerful mill and a strong wind. (March 1992)

Left: The miller (with clogs) at Het Prinsenhof is standing in the bin into which the husks and dust pass. The barley remains in the space between the stones and side of the grater from where it will fall into the bins after the gate has been opened. (March 1992)

Flax Scutching Mill

Right: The hollow post mill for scutching flax at Kortrijk in Belgium has a very large thatched buck. (August 1980)

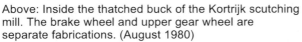

Above: Inside the thatched buck of the Kortrijk scutching mill. The brake wheel and upper gear wheel are separate fabrications. (August 1980)

Right: The wooden gearing on the windshaft engages with the wallower on top of the crown tree of the hollow post of the Kortrijk scutching mill. (August 1980)

Left top: The great spur wheel at the bottom of the vertical shaft under the paired cross trees supporting the buck of the Kortrijk scutching mill. (August 1980)

Left bottom: Retted flax drying before being scutched. (August 1980)

Right: Scutching stalls in the Kortrijk Mill. Bundles of flax would be passed through the slot in the board to be beaten by the revolving wooden blades to knock off the pith, leaving the fibres. (August 1980)

Chalk Grinding Mill

Left: Cliff Mill at Hessel near Hull has been preserved to show where chalk was ground to make whiting. Built between 1806 and 1825 to replace an earlier horse mill, it worked by wind until 1925. The five sails were fitted with roller reefing shutters and air brakes. (July 1990)

Below: A pair of edge runners faced with iron at Cliff Mill. Chalk was brought to the mill and broken into hand-sized lumps with sledgehammers. The lumps were shovelled into the crushing pan in which rotated the edge runners set vertically. Water was added and the slurry run off into settling pits. The ground chalk was lifted out of the pits and placed in drying sheds, now demolished. (July 1990)

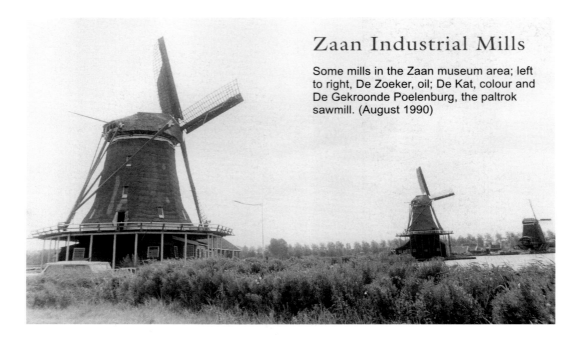

Zaan Industrial Mills

Some mills in the Zaan museum area; left to right, De Zoeker, oil; De Kat, colour and De Gekroonde Poelenburg, the paltrok sawmill. (August 1990)

Oil Mills

Left: The De Zoeker oil mill running with a pair of sails reefed to dagger point. (August 1990)

Right: The oil mill, De Bonte Hen, in the Zaan museum area with warehouse and 'convenience'. (August 1990)

Above: Cant posts, framing and thatching inside De Bonte Hen oil mill. (March 1992)

Right: The huge oil mill above Stockholm harbour is clad with copper sheathing on the sides of the smock portion and wooden boarding on the lower parts. (July 1975)

The seeds from plants such as cole or flax were first crushed by kollergangs. Wooden guides pushed the seeds back underneath the stones. To start this kollergang with its immense weight of the stones in De Bonte Hen, the sails were allowed to rotate slowly and then the kollergang gears were put in mesh, which might easily strip the wooden teeth. (March 1992)

Above left: In De Bonte Hen, the sails also operated a camshaft for raising stampers. (March 1992)
Above right: The crushed seeds were heated, put in a woollen bag which was wrapped in a strong cover woven from horsehair. A pair of these packages were placed in the cavity of a massive press block and secured with wedges. Fifty strokes from one stamper against a taper wedge squeezed out most of the oil. The pressing stamper is on the right with the wedge having pressed out the oil at De Bonte Hen. The double taper wedge is to the left which will be hit to release the packages. Note the earmuffs hanging on the left of the framing for this was a very noisy operation. (March 1992)
Below: The pressing block in the Stockholm oil mill with pressing stamper on the right and releasing wedge to the left. A pan under the pressing block would catch the oil. (August 1974)

Right: The pressed block of seed cake would be taken to these pot holes and broken up by stampers for pressing a second time. The ropes hold the tappets on the stampers out of mesh with the cams at De Bonte Hen. (March 1992)

Left: The pot hole and stampers in the Stockholm oil mill. (August 1974)

Colour Mill

Right: De Kat Mill in the Zaan museum area grinds colours for paints first beneath kollergangs and then stampers. The mill is working with only one pair of sails clothed. (August 1990)

Left: A variety of gears on the vertical shaft and other drives taken when De Kat Mill was working. (August 1990)

Right: A horse operated kollergang in the Arnhem Open Air Museum. (June 1972)

Left: The camshaft and stamper shafts with their tappets in De Kat Mill. (August 1990)

Papermaking Mill

De Schoolmeester, West Zaan, is the last surviving wind-powered paper mill, built in 1692. It is kept in full working order and paper is made there. (March 1992)

Left: Linen or cotton rags were delivered by barge through the doors at the end of the mill. (August 1990)

Below: The canal is at one end of the range of buildings. The process follows through to the drying sheds on the right. (June 1972)

Left: The rags are kept in storage bins according to their types. (August 1990)

Below: The materials are weighed before processing. (March 1992)

Left: All the power-driven machinery is concentrated beneath the tower of the thatched smock mill. The miller is setting a sail to start work. (August 1990)

Above left: The rags are dropped into the kapperij, a tub which rotates slowly as knives on the ends of stampers cut them up. (June 1972)

Above right: Some rags will be pulped under the massive edge runners of the kollergang. One runner is set closer to the vertical drive shaft so that the whole of the pan is covered. (June 1972)

Below: The great spur wheel at the bottom of the vertical shaft with drives to the Hollander beaters and other machines in the mill. (June 1972)

Two Hollander beaters at the bottom of the vertical shaft. The Dutch developed the Hollander or roll beater towards the end of the seventeenth century. It prepared the pulp more quickly than the previous stampers. (August 1990)

Gear drive on a beater shaft. (June 1992)

One beater was replaced in 1992. Here the breast is being carved in one side of the oval trough. There would be a central division in the middle of the trough. A bronze or iron bedplate fitted at the bottom of the breast against which bars round the roll would beat the rags and lift them over the breast to circulate them round and round until they were pulped. (June 1992)

The central division being fitted in the trough. (June 1992)

Bars are being fitted to the roll. (June 1992)

Originally paper was made by hand, sheet by sheet, but around 1900 a simple form of Fourdrinier papermaking machine was installed at De Schoolmeester. (August 1990)

Left: Pulp pours out of the headbox at the far end of the machine onto the moving gauze wire where most of the water drains out. (June 1972)

Below left: As the large couch roll turns, pulp builds up on its surface to the correct thickness for a sheet. The papermaker draws a knife across a slot in the roll to cut the sheet which he lifts off. (June 1972)

Below right: The papermaker lays off the wet sheets into a pile on the laystool. (June 1972)

Above: More water will be squeezed out in the wet press. It will be screwed down very firmly by inserting a lever which is tensioned by a rope from the Samson post on the right. (August 1990)

Left: The still damp paper is hung over ropes to dry in the drying loft. (August 1990)

Below: The paper may be flattened and smoothed by being passed between calender rolls. (March 1992)

The paper will be sorted on the bench on the left of the salle before being pressed again and stored with weights on top to flatten it.
(August 1990)

Right: The dry screw press is used for flattening paper. (August 1990)

Below: A papermaking mill such as De Schoolmeester with all its process buildings and drying loft had to be kept low so that the wind could reach the sails. (August 1990)

14. Windmills Adapted for Reuse

With their substantial brick or masonry towers, many windmills have survived long after their working days had ended. Slow decay set in so that sails fell off and caps deteriorated letting in the rain. But may have been rescued and converted for some further use, particularly those in rural areas which make desirable, if unusual dwellings. Additions range from the banal and ugly to accurate recreations of what the mill was like in its heyday. Such well-restored and preserved mills certainly add distinction to their areas.

Above: The mill built into the gatehouse of St. Benet's Abbey, was constructed around 1735 to crush coleseed for oil for lamps. It was adapted later as a drainage mill. A photo of 1856 shows staging at the present top of the medieval arches. It was fitted with two common and two patent sails but winded by a braced tailpole in Dutch fashion. The cap and sails were blown off in 1863 when it was tailwinded. (March 1990)

Left: Part of the medieval arch inside the St. Benet's Abbey Mill. (March 1990)

Above left: The mill in the grounds of Gordonstoun school is now a dovecote. (August 1991)

Above right: The tower of the windmill on the hill above the Clifton suspension bridge at Bristol has been turned into a camera obscura. (June 1991)

Below: At Ingham, a brick tower mill built around 1763 was unusually replaced by the present brick tower in 1872. The mill worked until 1933. It was used by the Ministry of Defence as a Royal Observer Corps post during World War II. (March 1990)

This brick mill at Hindringham had replaced an earlier post mill by 1845. Last worked in 1908, it lay derelict for many years until converted into a desirable cottage down a quiet country lane. (March 1990)

Above: The bank of the River Yare nearly obscures the bungalow added at the bottom of Langley Marsh Mill when seen from the Berney Arms Mill. (March 1990)

Right: While the reconstruction of the scoopwheel housing is to be applauded on the mill at Norton Marshes, the new cap might have been designed more appropriately. The mill was built in 1863. (August 1990)

Above left: The conversion of the mill at Stretham, Isle of Ely, has been completed with the addition of a fantail and skeleton sails since this photograph was taken in May 1990. The pulley wheel for driving the stones by some external engine has been retained. (May 1990)

Above right: Gibbet Hill Mill at the bottom end of the Wirral was a squat design typical of mills in the North West. Two common and two spring sails have been added as part of the conversion. (June 1990)

Left: The tower of Weybourne Mill has only a gentle batter. Built in about 1850, it lay derelict from the 1920s until bought in 1967. During conversion to a residence, the adjoining building was raised, so preventing the sails from working. (March 1990)

Above left: The mill at Cley-next-the-Sea has been the subject of many paintings and photographs. It was described as 'newly erected' in June 1819 but had ceased milling by 1912. It was turned into a holiday home in 1921 and a guesthouse in 1983. It has been listed Grade II. (March 1990)

Above right: Mautby Marsh Mill has been well restored except for the scoopwheel which was on the right hand side of the tower. (March 1990)

Below left: But alas the sails on Mautby Marsh Mill cannot turn owing to the cottage added onto the side of the tower. (March 1990)

Below right: An impressive little smock mill stands at the entrance to Rye when driving from the west. It was in fact built in 1932 as part of the terms of tenure of the bakery on the site because an earlier mill had been destroyed a couple of years previously. The cap is fixed rigidly to the body and the sails and fantail are dummies. (January 1968)

Glossary

Appold Turbine Centrifugal pump to raise water.

Archimedes screw Ancient water raising device invented by the Greek, Archimedes.

Back stays Strengthening supports at the back of the sail frame between sail bar and stock.

Bar (sail) Lateral member of sail frame.

Batter Slope on the walls of a tower or smoce mill from base to top.

Bay Space between two sail bars.

Bed stone The lower, fixed stone of a pair of horizontal millstones.

Bell alarm Device to warn the miller when the grain is running low.

Bill (mill) Double-ended steel chisel used for dressing stones.

Bin Container for grain in the upper floor of a mill.

Blades Parts of sails on which the wind operates.

Blue stone One-piece millstone imported from Germany.

Bolter, boulter Early type of machine for separating flour from bran by power-assisted sifting through a bolting cloth.

Brace Additional side pole to help strengthen the tailpole, probably originating on Dutch smock or tower mills.

Brake Lever-operated device working on the rim of the brake wheel to stop the sails.

Brake wheel Primary gearwheel mounted on the windshaft on the rim of which the band brake works.

Breast Front of the mill, normally a post mill.

Breast beam Main beam at the front of the mill or cap taking the weight of the windshaft.

Bridge tree Pivoted beam supporting a stone spindle.

Bridging box Adjustable bearing for the bottom of the stone spindle on the bridge tree.

Buck Body of a post mill.

Burr Hard coarse stone imported from France for making millstones.

Canister or cannister See poll end.

Cant post Corner post of a smock mill.

Cap Movable top of a tower or smock mill which turns on a curb on top of the tower to bring the sails into the wind.

Cap centring wheels Metal wheels to maintain the cap centrally within the curb.

Cap frame Main base frame of a cap.

Cap spars Rafters of a cap.

Clasp arm Method of constructing a wheel, the arms of which form a square to grip the shaft.

Cloth or clothing Fabric covering for common sails.

Collar Steadies the body of a post mill on the post.

Common sail The traditional sail covered with cloth.

Compass arm Method of constructing a wheel with radial spokes mortised into the shaft.

Cracking Fine lines dressed into the lands of a mill stone, also called stitching.

Cross Casting mounted on the end of the windshaft to carry the sails on its arms.

Cross tree Main horizontal beams in the sub-structure of a post mill.

Crown tree Horizontal beam which bears the weight of the buck of a post mill on the post.

Curb Track on the top of a smock or tower mill on which the cap turns.

Dagger point Second of four positions for spreading a sail cloth.

Damsel Device for agitating the shoe to deliver grain into the stones for milling.

Dead curb The cap slides round on wood or metal plates without the use of rollers.

Dressing Re-cutting the mill stones so they grind more efficiently.

Driving side Trailing side of the sail.

Edge runner Vertical millstone with horizontal axle used for crushing, also called kollergang.

Eye Hole in the centre of the runner stone into which the grain is fed.

Eye Facing directly into the wind.

Fan or fan tail Sail which automatically turns the mill into the wind, sometime called a fly.

First reef Sail shortened one setting.

Footstep Bearing supporting the bottom bearing of an upright shaft.

French burr Built-up mill stone used for flour.

Full sail Fully extended cloth on sail.

Furrows Grooves cut into the grinding surface of a millstone to lead the meal outwards.

Gallery Platform around the cap of a tower or smock mill.

Girts Main horizontal construction beam in a buck.

Glut box Used for throwing a stone nut on a quant out of gear.

Governor Automatic device to control the distance between the mill stones when milling or the speed of the mill.

Great spur wheel Gearwheel mounted on the upright shaft which drives the stone nuts.

Gudgeon Iron pin projecting from the end of a shaft to form a bearing.

Harp One of nine grinding areas of a millstone.

Hollow post mill Mill in which the drive is taken by a shaft through the central post to the machinery below.

Hopper Grain container mounted over the millstones.

Horizontal windmill The sails revolve in a horizontal plane on a vertical shaft.

Horse Framework on top of the stone casing supporting the hopper and shoe.

Jog-scry Inclined sieves to grade flour.

Kollergang Dutch name for vertical millstones.

Ladles Boards fitted to a scoopwheel to raise water, also called scoops.

Land Raised portions between the furrows of a millstone.

Lantern gear Early form of gearwheel in which a circle of staves held between two wooden flanges served the purpose of cogs or teeth. It was usually associated with a driving gear fitted with peg-like cogs which meshed with the staves of the lantern gear. It could be used to transmit power between two shafts either parallel or at right angles.

Laths Light longitudinal timbers on sail frames.

Leading board Longitudinal boards fitted along the leading sides of sails, often to improve the aerodynamics.

Live curb Curb fitted with rollers so it turns more easily.

Mace Connecting piece between the top of the spindle and rhynd.

Meal Product obtained after grinding.

Meal spout Conveys the meal from the stones to the sacks or meal bins.

Mill mound Generally any raised ground upon which a windmill was erected.

Multi-sailed Windmill with more than four sails.

Neck journal Front bearing surface of a windshaft, turning in a neck bearing. The bearing surface of the neck would generally be iron, the bearing being made of stone, wood or metal.

Overdrift millstones driven from above.

Paint staff Wooden straight-edge used to check the millstones while dressing.

Patent sail Self-regulating sail with shutters.

Peak stone Millstone quarried from millstone grit in Derbyshire; sometimes termed greystone.

Petticoat Vertical boarding around the lower part of a cap or post mill.

Pit wheel Large gearwheel on the shaft of a scoopwheel.

Pointing lines Cords attached to sail cloths on a common sail for reefing.

Poll end or canister Cast iron fitting on the end of the windshaft into which the sail stocks are fitted. It consists of two iron boxes at right angles to each other; formerly the stocks were mortised through the end of a timber windshaft.

Post Central pillar supporting the buck of a post mill.

Quant Spindle carrying the stone nut which drives an overdrift stone.

Quartering Turning the sails at a right angle to the wind.

Quarter bars Diagonal timbers in the substructure of a post mill which brace the post from the cross trees.

Quern Set of hand-driven millstones.

Raddle Substance made from red oxide and water or fat applied to the paint staff when dressing the stones to mark high places.

Reefing Reducing the area of a cloth sail exposed to the wind.

Rhynd, rind, rynd Metal cross let into the runner stone to take the drive and support the stone.

Roundhouse Structure below the buck to protect the trestle of a post mill and provide storage.

Runner stone Upper driven stone of a pair of millstones.

Sack hoist Wind-powered mechanism for raising sacks to the top of the mill.

Sails Parts of the mill energised by wind-pressure to drive machinery.

Scoops Blades on a scoopwheel which raise the water.

Shades Term sometimes used for shutters.

Sheer beams Two main timbers extending from breast to tail forming the bottom of a post mill buck; also the equivalent timbers in a cap.

Shoe Feeds grain from the hopper to the eye of the runner stone.

Shutters Hinged parts of a spring or patent sail which catch the wind.

Side girts Timbers running the full length at the sides of the buck.

Single-shuttered sails Having shutters on the trailing side only.

Smock mill Tower mill made with a wooden framework.

Spider Operates the shutter bars on patent sails.

Spring sails Shuttered sails in which the shutters in each sail are controlled by springs.

Starts Timbers in a scoopwheel which support the scoops.

Stitching Fine dressing on the lands of a millstone.

Stocks Timbers to which the sails are fixed passing through a poll end. A four-sailed mill normally has two stocks, each of which is passed half-way through the poll end and wedged in place. Each stock carries a sail at each end.

Stones Grind the flour.

Stone casing Light wooden case enclosing the millstones.

Stone nut Final driven pinion in the drive to the stones. In an overdrift mill, this gear is mounted on the quant; in an underdrift, on the stone spindle.

Striking gear Operates the shutters of patent sails.

Striking rod Passes from end to end of the windshaft to actuate the shutters of patent sails.

Sweep Southern name for sails.

Sword point Sail cloth reefed in narrow, pointed shape, the position with minimum cloth.

Tail Rear of the mill.

Tail beam Supports the tail bearing of a windshaft.

Tailpole Used to turn windmills to face the eye of the wind.

Tail wind Wind hitting the backs of the sails.

Tail winded A mill caught facing the wrong way.

Talthur Lever on the side of a post mill tailpole used to raise the ladder when turning the mill.

Tentering Adjusting the gap between millstones.

Thrift Handle which hold the mill bills and picks.

Thrust block Carries the bottom bearing of a shaft.

Tower mill Brick or masonry towers of which only the cap rotates to bring the sails into the wind.

Trestle Supporting sub-structure of a post mill.

Trolley wheels Used to support the cap on the curb.

Truck wheels Centre the cap of a tower or smock mill.

Trundle wheel Wooden gearwheel with pegs instead of cogs.

Tun Another name for the stone casing.

Underdrift Runner stone driven from below.

Upright or vertical shaft Main shaft driven by the wallower and carrying the great spur wheel.

Vanes Term sometimes used for the shutters in a sail, particularly the blades in the fan tail.

Vertical windmill The sails rotate in a vertical plane on a near-horizontal shaft.

Vat Another name for the stone casing.

Wallower First driven gear on top of the vertical shaft which meshes with the brake wheel.

Weather Twist along the driving side of a sail.

Wheel and chain Mechanism which turns the cap from the outside.

Whip The timber which is bolted to the stock and to which the bars and laths of the sail frame are fixed.

Winding Turning the cap of a tower or smock mill or the buck of a post mill so that the sails face squarely into the wind.

Windshaft Shaft carrying the sails at its outer end on which the brake wheel is mounted. It is inclined towards the back of the mill in order to distribute some of the load of the sails into the mill structure.

Wire machine Machine used to dress or separate flour from meal into several qualities by brushing the ground meal through wire gauze.

'Y' wheel Wheel with 'Y'-shaped forks around the rim to give the rope or chain increased grip.

Select Bibliography

Apling, H. *Norfolk Corn and Other Industrial Windmills*, Norfolk Windmills Trust, Norwich, 1984.

Batten, M.I., *English Windmills*, Vol. 1, Society for Protection of Ancient Buildings, Architectural Press, London, 1930; Vol. 2, by Smith, D., 1932.

Beedell, S., *Windmills*, David & Charles, Newton Abbot, 1975.

Blom, L.H., *The Tjasker Windmill*, The International Molinological Society, Netherlands, 1975.

Brown, R.J., *Windmills of England*, R. Hale, London, 1976, reprinted 1989.

Buckland, S., *Lee's Patent Windmill, 1744 – 1747*, Wind & Watermill Section, Society for Protection of Ancient Buildings, London, 1987.

Dolman, P., *Lincolnshire Windmills, A Contemporary Survey*, Lincolnshire County Council, Lincoln, 1986.

Douch, H.L., *Cornish Windmills*, O. Blackford, Truro, 1963.

Douglas, G., Oglethorpe, M. & Hume, J.R., *Scottish Windmills, A Survey*, Scottish Industrial Archaeology Survey, University of Strathclyde, 1984.

Farries, K.G., *Essex Windmills, Millers & Millwrights*, C. Skilton, London, 5 Vols., 1981 – 1988.

Farries, K.G. & Mason, R.T., *The Windmills of Surrey and Inner London*, C. Skilton, London, 1966.

Finch, W.C., *Watermills and Windmills, A Historical Survey of their Rise, Decline and Fall as Portrayed by those of Kent*, C.W. Daniel, 1933, new edn. A. Cassell, Sheerness, 1976.

Flint, B., *Windmills of East Anglia*, F.W. Pawsey, Ipswich, 1977.

Flint, B., *Suffolk Windmills*, Boydell Press, Woodbridge, 1979.

Freese, S., *Windmills and Millwrighting*, Cambridge University Press, 1957, reprint David & Charles, Newton Abbot, 1971.

Foreman, W., *Oxfordshire Mills*, Phillimore, Chichester, 1983.

Gregory, R., *East Yorkshire Windmills*, C. Skilton, Cheddar, 1985.

Gregory, R., *The Industrial Windmill in Britain*, Phillimore, Chichester, 2005.

Guise, B. & Lees, G., *Windmills of Anglesey*, Attic Books, Builth Wells, 1992.

Harverson, M., *Persian Windmills*, The International Molinological Society, Reading, 1991.

Hills, R.L., *The Drainage of the Fens*, Landmark, Ashbourne, 2003.

Hills, R.L., *Power from Wind, A History of Windmill Technology*, Cambridge University Press, 1994, reprint 1996.

Holt, *The Mills of Medieval England*, B. Blackwell, Oxford, 1988.

Hopkins, R.T., *Old Watermills and Windmills*, P. Allen, London, 1930, new edn. E.P. Publishing, Wakefield, 1976.

McDermott, R. & R., *The Standing Windmills of East Sussex*, Betford, Worthing, 1978.

McDermott, R. & R., *The Standing Windmills of West Sussex*, Betford, Worthing, 1978.

Mais, S.P.B., *England of the Windmills*, J.M. Dent, London, 1931, reprint E.P. Publishing, Wakefield, 1978.

Reynolds, J., *Windmills and Watermills*, H. Evelyn, London, 1970, reprint 1974.

Scott, M., *The Restoration of Windmills and Windpumps in Norfolk*, Norfolk Windmills, Trust, Norwich., 1977.

Skilton, C.P., *British Windmills and Watermills*, Collins, London, 1948.

Smith, A.C., *Drainage Windmills of the Norfolk Marshes*, Smith, Stevenage, new edn. 1990.

Stokhuizen, F., *The Dutch Windmill*, C.A.J. van Dishoeck, Bussum, Netherlands, 1962.

Wailes, R., *The English Windmill*, Routledge & Kegan Paul, London, 1954.

Watts, M., *Wiltshire Windmills*, Wiltshire Library & Museum Service, Trowbridge, 1980.

Gazetter & Index, Foreign Windmills

General Index

Drainage of the Fens

Rev. Dr Richard Hills

The story of the struggle to drain Fenland. A comprehensive study using many primary sources of research. The author brings his authoritative knowledge on industrial machinery to produce the definitive work on the history of and the methods of land drainage, from early windmills to powerful steam engines. The influence of improved drainage on the agriculture, commerce and way of life of the region is very much a part of the text.

205pp; 136 illustrations; hardback
PRICE: £19.95. ISBN: 1-84306-074-4. This book has sold well, we have limited stock left.

Pumping Engines of the Fens

K.S.G. Hinde

A record of some 220 pumping stations lying between Cambridge and the Humber, from the early-19th to mid-20th century. The history and location of each station is recorded. The complex system of drainage boards is explained. A work of reference for local historians, steam enthusiasts and industrial archaeologists. Many illustrations have not previously been published. A companion volume to Drainage of the Fens.

Approx 192pp; perhaps 300 illustrations; hardback
PUBLICATION: August 2005. PRICE: £19.99. ISBN: 1-84306-188-0.

James Watt : Volume 1. His time in Scotland, 1736-1774

Rev. Dr. Richard Hills

"destined for a long shelf life" – Journal of the Institute of Mechanical Engineers.
A detailed account of Watt's early life and work in Scotland prior to his move to Birmingham in 1774. Chapters include, The Formative Years; from Instrument Maker to Engineer; Chemical Engineer; Civil Engineer; Engineer of Steam Engines; Enter Mathew Boulton; 13-page bibliography; index.

246 x 174mm. 480pp plus a 16pp photographic section; hardback.
PRICE: £37.50. ISBN: Vol 1: 1-84306-045-0.

James Watt: Volume 2. The Years of Toil 1775-1785

Rev. Dr. Richard Hills

Covers: Watt's move to Birmingham; Prototype engines and The Patent Act, 1775; Continuing Trials and The First Engines; Family and Partners, 1774-80s; Fair Prospects in Cornwall; Development of the Single-Acting Pumping Engines and Foreign Patents; The Financial Struggle; Problems in Cornwall; Natural Philosopher; Epilogue.

256pp; approx 55 illustrations; hardback
PRICE: £26.99. ISBN: 1-84306-046-9.

James Watt: Volume 3. Triumph Through Adversity 1785-1819

Rev. Dr. Richard Hills

Covers: Watt's Later Engine Patents; Rotative Engines; Family Tribulations; The Manufacture of Chlorine and Medicinal Gases; Rivals and Pirates; Patent Trials; Retirement.

About 256pp; approx 70 illustrations; hardback
PUBLICATION: November 2005. PRICE: c. £26.99. ISBN: 1-84306-193-7.

Life and Inventions of Richard Roberts 1789-1864

Rev. Dr. Richard Hills

Although little known, Robert's was one of the country's greatest inventors and the father of production engineering; in advance of Whitworth in enlarging the scope and accuracy of machine tools. In 1821, he made the first machine for manufacturing industrial gears (for textile machines). Soon after he made a power loom and the first self-acting spinning mule (the first feed back control system), revolutionising the industry. He ran Sharp, Roberts in Manchester, one of the largest railway loco builders in the world. The first suggestion for twin screwed ships driven independently came from Roberts. He designed the machine for punching rivet holes in metal plates, first used on the Britannia Bridge across the Manai Strait. This is the first full length biography of the man and his 25 patents. It looks at his life and inventions in the world of machine tools; the gas meter; textiles; road vehicles; locos; horology and ship building. Profusely illustrated, with an extensive bibliography and fully referenced.

246 x 174mm. 256pp and 8pp photograpic section; hardback.
PRICE: £29.95 ISBN: 1-84306-027-2

LANDMARK
Publishing Ltd ● ● ● ●

Ashbourne Hall, Cokayne Ave, Ashbourne, Derbyshire, DE6 1EJ, England
Tel 01335 347349, Fax 01335 347303, e-mail landmark@clara.net